P2 Improving Skills

by
Shaun Armstrong and Chris Huffer

Solomon Press

Published by Solomon Press
Unit 1, Rydon Farm, West Newton,
Somerset, TA7 0BZ

Tel: 01278 661 300
E-mail: info@solomon-press.com
Website: www.solomon-press.com

The *Advanced Study Series* is a trade mark of Solomon Press

© S Armstrong C Huffer 2001
First published 2001

ISBN 1901724263

Design and typesetting by S Armstrong and Pedeke Ltd, Bridgwater, Somerset.
Printed in Great Britain by S & G Print Group, Merthyr Tydfil, Wales.

CONTENTS

Rational Expressions

Exercise 1S   Skills Practice

1   Simplify

    a $\dfrac{9}{6x-3}$
    b $\dfrac{x^3-2x}{3x+x^2}$
    c $\dfrac{2t-4}{t^2-3t+2}$
    d $\dfrac{3x-9}{x^2-9}$

    e $\dfrac{y^2-y-2}{2y^2-4y}$
    f $\dfrac{2a^2+4a-6}{a^2+5a+6}$
    g $\dfrac{2x^2-9x+4}{2x^2-6x-8}$
    h $\dfrac{30+21x+3x^2}{12-6x-6x^2}$

2   Express as a single fraction in its simplest form.

    a $\dfrac{x}{2x+10}\times\dfrac{x+5}{x-3}$
    b $\dfrac{y+3}{y^2-4y}\times\dfrac{6y^2}{y^2-9}$

    c $\dfrac{2x^2}{2x+1}\div\dfrac{4x^3}{x-1}$
    d $\dfrac{4x+8}{2x^2-2}\div\dfrac{3x+6}{x^2+x}$

    e $\dfrac{4a^2+2a}{a^2-4a+3}\times\dfrac{a^2-a-6}{2a^2-a-1}$
    f $\dfrac{x^2-4x-5}{x^2-x-2}\div\dfrac{3x^2-16x+5}{x^2-4}$

3   Express as a single fraction in its simplest form.

    a $\dfrac{2}{t}+\dfrac{5}{t-1}$
    b $\dfrac{3x}{x+3}-\dfrac{x-2}{x+1}$

    c $\dfrac{3}{2x-4}+\dfrac{2x}{2x^2-5x+2}$
    d $\dfrac{5}{x^2-3x}+\dfrac{8}{x^2-9}$

    e $\dfrac{3}{y^2+2y-8}-\dfrac{1}{2y^2+8y}$
    f $\dfrac{4x+1}{2x-1}+\dfrac{3}{x^2-4}-\dfrac{2x}{x+2}$

4   Solve

    a $\dfrac{1}{x-1}+\dfrac{2x}{x-4}=\dfrac{x-3}{x-1}$
    b $\dfrac{x}{x+2}=\dfrac{3x-15}{x^2-x-20}$

    c $\dfrac{x^2+4x}{x^2+3x-4}\div\dfrac{x^2+2x}{x^2-4}=\dfrac{5}{2}$
    d $\dfrac{3x-3x^2}{x^2-3x+2}-\dfrac{2+x}{3-x}=0$

5   Express y explicitly in terms of x.

    a $\dfrac{1}{2-y}=\dfrac{3}{x+4}$
    b $\dfrac{2}{x}+\dfrac{1}{y}=\dfrac{4}{x-3}$

    c $\dfrac{x+1}{x+2}=\dfrac{x-3}{y+1}+\dfrac{4}{x+2}$
    d $\dfrac{2x-1}{y-3}=\dfrac{2x^2+x-1}{3x^2+5x+2}$

6   Simplify

    a $\left(\dfrac{2}{x-3}+\dfrac{x+1}{x^2-3x}\right)\times\dfrac{x^2+2x}{3x^2+10x+3}$
    b $\dfrac{6x-2}{x^2+2x}\div\left(\dfrac{2x-4}{x^2+1}+\dfrac{7}{x+2}\right)$

Exercise 1E   Exam Practice

1   Express

$$\frac{t+2}{t} + \frac{4}{t^2-2t} - \frac{3}{t-2}$$

as a single fraction in its simplest form.   **(5 marks)**

2   **a**   Simplify $\dfrac{x^3+4x^2-5x}{2x^2+7x-15}$.   **(3 marks)**

     b   Find the value of x for which

$$\frac{x^3+4x^2-5x}{2x^2+7x-15} \div \frac{x^2-4x}{2x-3} = \frac{1}{3}.$$ **(5 marks)**

3   **a**   Given that $\dfrac{3}{2y+5} = \dfrac{x+2}{2x^2+3x-2}$,

     show that $y = ax + b$ where a and b are integers to be found.   **(5 marks)**

     b   Given also that

$$\frac{3}{z} = \frac{x-1}{2x^2-5x+3},$$

     show that $z = 2y - 1$.   **(5 marks)**

4   **a**   Show that $(x - 3)$ is a factor of $(x^3 + 2x^2 - 11x - 12)$.   **(2 marks)**

     b   Hence, simplify the expression

$$\frac{x^3+2x^2-11x-12}{2x^2-3x-5}.$$ **(5 marks)**

5   Solve the equation

$$\frac{x+4}{x^2+x-12} - \frac{x}{x+2} = 0,$$

giving your answers in the form $a + b\sqrt{6}$.   **(7 marks)**

6   **a**   Given that

$$\frac{1}{y-2} - \frac{1}{y+2} = \frac{2x}{x-1},$$

     show that

$$y^2 = \frac{6x-2}{x}.$$ **(5 marks)**

     b   Hence, solve the simultaneous equations

$$\frac{1}{y-2} - \frac{1}{y+2} = \frac{2x}{x-1},$$

$$\frac{8}{y^2} = \frac{x+3}{2}.$$ **(7 marks)**

Recurrence Relations

Exercise 2S   Skills Practice

1   Use the given recurrence relation and first term, u_1, to find the second, third and fourth terms of each sequence.

    a $u_n = u_{n-1} + 3, \quad n > 1, \quad u_1 = 4$ **b** $u_n = 3u_{n-1}, \quad n > 1, \quad u_1 = 2$

    c $u_n = 2u_{n-1} + 1, \quad n > 1, \quad u_1 = 0$ **d** $u_n = \frac{1}{2}u_{n-1} + 4, \quad n > 1, \quad u_1 = 6$

    e $u_n = 4u_{n-1} - 5, \quad n > 1, \quad u_1 = 3$ **f** $u_n = 8 - 2u_{n-1}, \quad n > 1, \quad u_1 = 5$

2   A sequence is defined as follows:

$$t_n = \frac{1}{2}(t_{n-1} + 3), \quad n > 1, \quad t_1 = 11.$$

    a   Show that $t_4 = 4$.   **b**   Find t_6.

3   Find a recurrence relation of the form $u_n = au_{n-1} + b, n > 1$, between the terms in each of the following sequences.

    a   20, 17, 14, 11, 8, 5, ...   **b**   0.08, 0.4, 2, 10, 50, 250, ...

    c   2, 3, 5, 9, 17, 33, ...   **d**   0, 1, 4, 13, 40, 121, ...

4   Use the given recurrence relation and first term, u_1, to find the second, third and fourth terms of each sequence.

    a $u_{n+1} = 5u_n - 3, \quad n \geq 1, \quad u_1 = 4$ **b** $u_{n+1} = 4(u_n - 2), \quad n \geq 1, \quad u_1 = 3$

    c $u_{n+1} = 1 + \frac{2}{3}u_n, \quad n \geq 1, \quad u_1 = 12$ **d** $u_{n+1} = 8 + 3u_n, \quad n \geq 1, \quad u_1 = {}^-2$

5   Find u_2, u_3, u_4 and u_5 and describe the behaviour of sequences defined as follows:

    a $u_n = \frac{1}{2}(u_{n-1} - 1), \quad n > 1, \quad u_1 = 0$ **b** $u_n = 4 - u_{n-1}, \quad n > 1, \quad u_1 = 6$

    c $u_n = 3u_{n-1} - 1, \quad n > 1, \quad u_1 = 1$ **d** $u_n = \frac{1}{4}(u_{n-1} + 9), \quad n > 1, \quad u_1 = 7$

6   Find the value of u_1 given that $u_4 = 33$ and that

$$u_{n+1} = 4u_n - 3, \quad n \geq 1.$$

7   Find expressions in terms of k for t_2 and t_3 in each of the following sequences.

    a $t_n = 3t_{n-1} + k, \quad n > 1, \quad t_1 = 2$ **b** $t_{n+1} = 2(3 - t_n), \quad n \geq 1, \quad t_1 = k$

    c $t_{n+1} = kt_n - 2, \quad n \geq 1, \quad t_1 = 1$ **d** $t_n = kt_{n-1} - 2k, \quad n > 1, \quad t_1 = 5$

8   A sequence is defined by the recurrence relation

$$u_{n+1} = 2u_n + k, \quad n \geq 1, \quad u_1 = 4.$$

    Given that $u_3 = 31$, find the value of k.

Exercise 2E   Exam Practice

1   The terms of a sequence are related by the recurrence relation

$$u_{n+1} = \tfrac{1}{4}(u_n + 3), \quad n \geq 1.$$

Given that $u_4 = 2$, find the value of

a u_5,   **(2 marks)**

b u_1.   **(3 marks)**

2   A sequence is defined by the recurrence relation

$$u_n = ku_{n-1} - 6, \quad n > 1, \quad u_1 = 4.$$

a   Find an expression for u_3 in terms of k.   **(3 marks)**

Given that $u_3 = 12$,

b   find the two possible values of k.   **(4 marks)**

3   A sequence is defined by the following recurrence relation

$$u_{n+1} = u_n + 3, \quad n \geq 1, \quad u_1 = 4.$$

a   Find the value of u_5.   **(3 marks)**

b   Evaluate $\displaystyle\sum_{r=5}^{30} u_r$.   **(4 marks)**

4   The third, fourth and fifth terms of a sequence are 4, 8 and 18 respectively. Given that the terms of the sequence are related by the recurrence relation

$$u_{n+1} = au_n + b,$$

a   find the values of a and b,   **(4 marks)**

b   find the seventh term of the sequence.   **(3 marks)**

5   The fourth term of a sequence is ‾1.4. Given that the terms of the sequence are related by the recurrence relation

$$u_{n+1} = \tfrac{2}{u_n} - 1,$$

a   find the third term of the sequence,   **(3 marks)**

b   show that the first term of the sequence is 4.   **(3 marks)**

6   A sequence is defined as follows:

$$t_n = \tfrac{1}{3}(t_{n-1} + k), \quad n > 1, \quad t_1 = 6.$$

a   Find and simplify expressions for t_2 and t_3 in terms of k.   **(3 marks)**

Given that $t_3 = 2t_2$,

b   show that $t_4 = ‾7$.   **(5 marks)**

Binomial Series

Exercise 3S   Skills Practice

1   Write down the expansion of $(1 + x)^3$.

2   Using your answer to question **1** find the expansion of

    a $(1 + 2x)^3$ **b** $(1 - x)^3$ **c** $(1 - 2x)^3$ **d** $(1 + \frac{1}{2}x)^3$

    e $(1 + 3y)^3$ **f** $(1 + y^2)^3$ **g** $(1 - 6y)^3$ **h** $(1 + 2y^4)^3$

3   Expand

    a $(1 + x)^4$ **b** $(1 + 3x)^4$ **c** $(1 - \frac{2}{3}x)^4$ **d** $(1 + \frac{2}{x})^4$

    e $(1 + x)^5$ **f** $(1 - 2x)^5$ **g** $(1 + 3x^2)^5$ **h** $(1 - x)^6$

4   **a** Express $(1 + \sqrt{3})^4$ in the form $A + B\sqrt{3}$.

    b Express $(1 - 3\sqrt{2})^5$ in the form $A + B\sqrt{2}$.

5   Find the first 4 terms in the expansion in ascending powers of x for

    a $(1 + x)^8$ **b** $(1 + x)^{16}$ **c** $(1 + x)^{20}$ **d** $(1 + 2x)^{11}$

6   Find the first 4 terms in the expansion in ascending powers of y for

    a $(1 + y)^9$ **b** $(1 - 2y)^6$ **c** $(1 - 3y)^{18}$ **d** $(1 + \frac{1}{2}y^2)^{10}$

7   **a** Expand $(1 + 2x)^7$ in ascending powers of x as far as the term in x^3.

    b Use your expansion with $x = 0.01$ to find the value of $(1.02)^7$ correct to 4 dp.

8   Find the coefficient of x^4 in the binomial expansion of

    a $(1 + x)^9$ **b** $(1 - 4x)^{12}$ **c** $(1 + 2x^2)^4$ **d** $(1 - \frac{1}{3}x^4)^8$

9   Expand

    a $(2 + x)^3$ **b** $(3 - y)^4$ **c** $(4 + 2x)^4$ **d** $(4 - \frac{1}{2}y)^5$

10   Find the first 4 terms in the expansion in ascending powers of x for

    a $(3 + x)^8$ **b** $(5 - x)^6$ **c** $(2 + 3x)^7$ **d** $(3 - \frac{1}{3}x)^{10}$

11   Find the coefficient of y^6 in the binomial expansion of

    a $(2 + y)^7$ **b** $(2 - y)^{15}$ **c** $(3 + 4y)^8$ **d** $(3 + y^2)^6$

12   Expand $(x + 2x^{-1})^4$ in descending powers of x.

Exercise 3E   Exam Practice

1   **a** Expand $(1 + 2x)^9$ in ascending powers of x as far as the term in x^3,
    simplifying the coefficient in each term.   **(4 marks)**

   b Using your series together with a suitable value of x, estimate the
    value of $(1.002)^9$ correct to 6 decimal places.   **(3 marks)**

2   **a** Find an expression in terms of n for the coefficient of x^2 in the
    binomial expansion of $(1 - \frac{2}{3}x)^n$, where n is a positive integer. **(2 marks)**

   Given that the coefficient of x^2 is 68,

   b find the value of n.   **(4 marks)**

3   Find the series expansion of

   a $(1 + x)^4$,   **(2 marks)**

   b $(1 - 2x)(1 + x)^4$,   **(3 marks)**

   c $(5 - 3x)^4$.   **(3 marks)**

4   In the binomial expansion of $(1 + kx)^8$, $k \neq 0$, the coefficients of the
   terms in x and x^2 are equal.

   a Find the value of k.   **(4 marks)**

   b Show that the coefficient of x^3 is $\frac{64}{49}$.   **(2 marks)**

5   **a** Expand $(2 + 3x)^6$ in ascending powers of x as far as the term in x^3,
    simplifying the coefficient in each term.   **(4 marks)**

   b Hence, find the coefficient of x^3 in the expansion of
   $$(1 - 4x)(2 + 3x)^6.$$ **(3 marks)**

6   **a** Find the first four terms in the binomial expansion of $(2 - \frac{1}{2}x)^8$
    in ascending powers of x.   **(4 marks)**

   b Use your series together with a suitable value of x to estimate the
    value of $(1.995)^8$ correct to 6 significant figures.   **(4 marks)**

7   Given that
   $$(1 + k\sqrt{2})^4 \equiv A + B\sqrt{2},$$

   a find expressions for A and B in terms of k.   **(4 marks)**

   Given also that $(1 + k\sqrt{2})^4 + (1 - k\sqrt{2})^4 = 226$,

   b show that $k^2 = 4$.   **(5 marks)**

Sequences and Series Review

Exercise 4E   Exam Practice

1   **a** Find the values of A, B and C for which

$$(1 - 4x)^{15} \equiv 1 + Ax + Bx^2 + Cx^3 + \dots$$ **(4 marks)**

    b Hence find the series expansion of $(2x - 1)(1 - 4x)^{15}$ in ascending powers of x as far as the term in x^3.   **(4 marks)**

2   A sequence is defined as follows:

$$u_n = 3u_{n-1} + k, \quad n > 1, \quad u_1 = 3.$$

    a Find and simplify expressions for u_2 and u_3 in terms of k.   **(3 marks)**

    Given that $u_2 + 2u_3 = 0$

    b find the value of k.   **(3 marks)**

3   **a** Expand $(2 + 3x)^5$ in ascending powers of x.   **(4 marks)**

    b Hence, find the coefficient of y^6 in the expansion of $(2 - 6y^2)^5$.   **(3 marks)**

4   **a** Expand $(1 - \frac{1}{2}x)^{16}$ in ascending powers of x as far as the term in x^3, simplifying the coefficient in each term.   **(4 marks)**

    b By substituting a suitable value for x, use your series to estimate the value of $(\frac{199}{200})^{16}$ correct to 4 significant figures.   **(4 marks)**

5   The terms of a sequence are related by the recurrence relation

$$u_{n+1} = \tfrac{3}{2}u_n, \quad n \geq 1.$$

    Given that $u_3 = 4.5$,

    a find the value of u_1,   **(3 marks)**

    b evaluate $\displaystyle\sum_{r=1}^{15} u_r$ correct to 2 decimal places.   **(4 marks)**

6   **a** Express $(1 - \sqrt{2})^5$ in the form $A + B\sqrt{2}$.   **(4 marks)**

    b Hence, express $(\frac{\sqrt{2}}{2+\sqrt{2}})^5$ in the form $A + B\sqrt{2}$.   **(4 marks)**

7   The terms of a sequence are related by the recurrence relation

$$u_{n+1} = 2u_n - 5, \quad n \geq 1.$$

    a Show that $u_4 = 8u_1 - 35$.   **(4 marks)**

    Given that $u_2 + u_3 + u_4 = 8$,

    b find the value of u_4.   **(4 marks)**

8   The first three terms in the binomial expansion of $(1 + ax)^b$ in ascending powers of x are as follows:

$$1 - 24x + 240x^2 + \ldots$$

Given that b is a positive integer,

    a   show that $b = 6$ and find the value of a,   **(6 marks)**

    b   find the next term in the expansion.   **(2 marks)**

9   **a**   Expand $(1 + 2x)^4$ in ascending powers of x.   **(4 marks)**

    b   By substituting suitable values of x into your expansion, show that

$$(1 + 2\sqrt{5})^4 + (1 - 2\sqrt{5})^4 = 1042.$$ **(4 marks)**

10   The terms of a sequence are related by the recurrence relation

$$x_{n+1} = px_n + 6, \quad n \geq 1.$$

Given that the third and fourth terms of the sequence are 8 and 10 respectively,

    a   find the value of p,   **(3 marks)**

    b   find the first term of the sequence.   **(3 marks)**

11   Find the coefficient of x^2 in the expansion of

    a $(1 + \frac{3}{4}x)^{32}$,   **(3 marks)**

    b $(1 + \frac{1}{2}x)(1 + \frac{3}{4}x)^{32}$.   **(4 marks)**

12   **a**   Expand $(\frac{x}{2} + \frac{2}{x})^4$ in descending powers of x.   **(4 marks)**

    b   Find the coefficient of x^2 in the expansion of $(\frac{x}{2} + \frac{2}{x})^8$.   **(3 marks)**

13   The terms of a sequence are related by the recurrence relation

$$u_{n+1} = u_n + \frac{4}{u_n}, \quad n \geq 1.$$

Given that $u_3 = 5$,

    a   find the value of u_4,   **(2 marks)**

    b   show that one possible value of u_2 is 1 and find the other possible value,   **(4 marks)**

    c   prove that if $u_2 = 1$, then u_1 does not exist.   **(4 marks)**

Given that u_1 exists,

    d   find the value of u_1.   **(3 marks)**

Laws of Logarithms

Exercise 5S   Skills Practice

1   Rewrite each statement in the form $\log_a b = c$.

    a $9^2 = 81$ **b** $10^3 = 1000$ **c** $3^5 = 243$

2   Rewrite each statement in the form $a^b = c$.

    a $\log_2 16 = 4$ **b** $\log_5 625 = 4$ **c** $\log_{10} 1\,000\,000 = 6$

3   State the value of

    a $\log_2 4$ **b** $\log_2 32$ **c** $\log_2 \frac{1}{2}$

    d $\log_3 27$ **e** $\log_4 \frac{1}{4}$ **f** $\log_8 64$

    g $\log_3 \frac{1}{9}$ **h** $\log_6 6$ **i** $\log_5 125$

    j $\log_7 1$ **k** $\log_9 3$ **l** $\log_5 0.2$

    m $\log_{16} 2$ **n** $\log_{10} 0.01$ **o** $\log_4 8$

4   Find the value of x for which

    a $\log_2 x = 6$ **b** $\log_5 x = 3$ **c** $\log_x 49 = 2$

    d $2\log_x 4 = 1$ **e** $\log_5 x = 0$ **f** $2\log_x 27 - 3 = 0$

5   Express in the form $a\log_5 x$

    a $\log_5 x^2$ **b** $3\log_5 x^4$ **c** $\log_5 \frac{1}{x}$

    d $2\log_5 \frac{1}{x^3}$ **e** $\log_5 \sqrt{x}$ **f** $6\log_5 \frac{1}{\sqrt{x}}$

6   Express in the form $\log_2 n$

    a $\log_2 3 + \log_2 5$ **b** $\log_2 9 - \log_2 3$ **c** $4\log_2 3$

    d $2\log_2 6 - \log_2 3$ **e** $1 + \log_2 7$ **f** $\log_2 20 - 2$

7   Evaluate

    a $\log_6 2 + \log_6 3$ **b** $\log_2 12 - \log_2 3$ **c** $\log_3 4 - 2\log_3 6$

    d $3\log_{10} 2 + \log_{10} 125$ **e** $\log_4 18 - \frac{1}{2}\log_4 81$ **f** $5\log_8 \frac{1}{2} - \frac{1}{4}\log_8 16$

8   Express in the form $a\log_{10} 2 + b\log_{10} 3$

    a $\log_{10} 12$ **b** $\log_{10} 54$ **c** $\log_{10} 8 - \log_{10} 6$

    d $3\log_{10} 6 - 4\log_{10} 2$ **e** $\log_{10} \frac{3}{4}$ **f** $\frac{1}{2}\log_{10} 9 + \frac{2}{3}\log_{10} 64$

Exercise 5E   Exam Practice

1   Find integers A and B such that

$$A \log_{10} 2 + \log_{10} 18 = B \log_{10} 3 + \log_{10} 48.$$ **(4 marks)**

2   Find, correct to 2 decimal places, the values of x for which

   a $3 \log_2 x = 10$,   **(2 marks)**

   b $\log_x 5 - 3 = 0$.   **(3 marks)**

3   A curve has the equation $y = p \log_2 x + q, x > 0$.

   Given that the curve passes through the points with coordinates
   $(2, {}^-1)$ and $(8, 5)$,

   a   find the values of p and q,   **(4 marks)**

   b   find the x-coordinate of the point where the curve crosses the
   x-axis giving your answer correct to 3 decimal places.   **(3 marks)**

4   The terms of a sequence are related by the recurrence relation

$$u_{n+1} = k \log_2 u_n + 2, \quad n \geq 1.$$

   Given that $u_3 = 8$ and $u_4 = 20$,

   a   find the value of k,   **(3 marks)**

   b   find the value of u_1.   **(4 marks)**

5   **a**   Prove that for all positive values of x

$$\log_a x^k \equiv k \log_a x.$$ **(4 marks)**

   b   Express

$$\log_a 16 - 3 \log_a \sqrt{2}$$

   in the form $k \log_a 2$, where k is an exact fraction.   **(3 marks)**

6   Solve the equation

$$\log_2 (5x - 4) = 6 \log_8 x$$ **(5 marks)**

7   **a**   Given that $p = \log_3 x$ and $q = \log_3 y$, find expressions in
   terms of p and q for

   i $\log_3 (x^3 y)$,

   ii $\log_3 \left(\frac{y^2}{x} \right)$.   **(4 marks)**

   b   Hence, or otherwise, solve the simultaneous equations

$$\log_3 (x^3 y) = 1$$

$$\log_3 \left(\frac{y^2}{x} \right) = 9$$ **(4 marks)**

e^x, ln x and a^x

Exercise 6S   Skills Practice

1   Find, correct to 4 sf, the value of

    a e^3 **b** e^6 **c** e **d** $2e^2$ **e** $e^{\frac{1}{2}}$ **f** lg 60

    g 3 lg 2   **h** lg $\frac{2}{3}$ **i** ln 3   **j** ln 0.01   **k** 2 ln 8   **l** $\frac{1}{4}$ ln 90

2   Write down the value of

    a $e^{\ln 5}$ **b** $e^{2\ln 4}$ **c** $3e^{\ln 1}$ **d** ln e   **e** ln e^3 **f** $2\ln e^{-4}$

3   Solve each equation, giving your answers in terms of e.

    a ln x = 2   **b** 3 ln y − 8 = 0   **c** ln (x + 1) = 6

    d 2 ln 4y = 10   **e** ln (2x − 5) − 2 = 0   **f** $6 - \ln(\frac{x+3}{2}) = 0$

4   Solve each equation, giving your answers in terms of logarithms.

    a $e^x = 3$ **b** $2e^y - 8 = 0$ **c** $12 - 2e^{\frac{1}{2}y} = 0$

    d $e^{3x-2} = 15$ **e** $3e^{x+4} = 7$ **f** $6e^{2x+5} - 9 = 0$

5   Find, correct to 2 dp, the value of x for which

    a $2e^x = 5$ **b** 2 lg x = lg 3   **c** 3 ln (x + 4) = 9

    d $17 - 2e^{4x+1} = 0$ **e** 16 − 4 ln (1 − 2x) = 0   **f** lg (x + 1) − lg (x − 1) = 1

    g $e^{x+3} = 2 - e^x$ **h** $e^{6x} = 3e^{x-3}$ **i** 2 + ln x = ln (x + 3)

6   Solve, giving your answers correct to 3 sf,

    a $3^x = 5$ **b** $2^y = 35$ **c** $18^x = 10$

    d $4^{y-1} = 60$ **e** $6 - 9^{x+3} = 0$ **f** $2(6^x) = 95$

    g $12^{2x-5} = 211$ **h** $100 - 4(2^{3x}) = 0$ **i** $5^y = 7^{y+2}$

    j $4^{3x} - 9^{x+5} = 0$ **k** $10^{y-1} = 2^{y+3}$ **l** $3^{x-2} = 3(2^x)$

7   **a** Given that $u = 2^x$, express $2^{2x} - 2^x - 6$ in terms of u.

    b Solve the equation $2^{2x} - 2^x - 6 = 0$, giving any answers correct to 2 dp.

8   Find, giving non-exact answers correct to 2 dp, the values of x for which

    a $3^{2x} - 3^x - 20 = 0$ **b** $8^{2x} + 8^x - 6 = 0$ **c** $2^{2x} - 8(2^x) + 12 = 0$

    d $4^{2x} - 6(4^x) = 16$ **e** $6^{2x} = 3(6^x + 18)$ **f** $5^{2x} - 5^{x+1} + 6 = 0$

    g $2^{2x} - 2^{x+2} + 3 = 0$ **h** $9^x(9^x + 5) = 14$ **i** $2^{2x+1} + 4 = 9(2^x)$

Exercise 6E   Exam Practice

1   Solve, giving your answers correct to 3 significant figures,

    a $6^x = 80$, **(3 marks)**

    b $10 - 4 \ln (x^2 - 2) = 0$. **(4 marks)**

2   By letting $u = 3^x$, or otherwise, solve the equation
$$3^{2x} - 3^{x+2} + 18 = 0,$$
    giving any answers to an appropriate degree of accuracy. **(6 marks)**

3   Given that
$$\ln (x + 4) + \ln 2x = 3,$$
    a show that x satisfies the equation
$$x^2 + 4x + k = 0,$$
       where k is a constant that you should find in terms of e, **(4 marks)**

    b show that $x = 1.75$, correct to 2 decimal places. **(3 marks)**

4   Solve the simultaneous equations
$$x - e^y + 10 = 0$$
$$2x + e^y - 4 = 0$$
    (4 marks)

5   Find, correct to 3 significant figures, the values of x for which

    a $e^{x-4} = 7$, **(2 marks)**

    b $\log_x 15 = 3$, **(3 marks)**

    c $2 \ln (3x - 1) + 5 = 0$. **(4 marks)**

6   Solve the equation
$$2^x(2^x + 1) = 30,$$
    giving any answers correct to 3 significant figures. **(5 marks)**

7   A cup of water is heated to 80°C and allowed to cool.

    The temperature, T °C, of the water t minutes after it starts to cool is given by
$$T = 25 + Ae^{-kt}.$$
    a Find the value of A. **(2 marks)**

    Given that $T = 50$ when $t = 6.5$,

    b find the value of k correct to 4 significant figures, **(4 marks)**

    c find the value of t, correct to the nearest minute, when $T = 30$. **(4 marks)**

Exponentials and Logarithms Review

Exercise 7E   Exam Practice

1   Given that for positive values of x and y

$$3 \log_a y - \tfrac{1}{2} \log_a x^3 = 0,$$

find the value of k such that $y = x^k$.   **(3 marks)**

2   Find, correct to 3 significant figures, the values of x and y for which

a $2 \ln x - 7 = 0,$ **(3 marks)**

b $3^y = 5^{2y-1}.$ **(4 marks)**

3   Find the integer values of A and B such that

$$\ln 160 - \ln 50 = A \ln 2 + B \ln 5.$$ **(4 marks)**

4   **a** By letting $p = \log_a x$ and $q = \log_a y$, or otherwise, prove that for all positive values of x and y

$$\log_a xy \equiv \log_a x + \log_a y.$$ **(4 marks)**

b Given that m and n are positive integers and that $m > n$, find the values of m and n such that

$$\log_3 m + \log_3 n = 1.$$ **(3 marks)**

5   The points with coordinates $(2, 0)$ and $(5, 1)$ lie on the curve with equation

$$y = \lg (ax + b).$$

Find the values of a and b.   **(4 marks)**

6   **a** Given that $y = 3^x$, express 3^{2x-1} in terms of y.   **(2 marks)**

b Solve the equation

$$2(1 - 3^{2x-1}) = 3^{x-1},$$

giving any answers correct to 3 significant figures.   **(5 marks)**

7   **a** Simplify

$$\ln a + \ln a^2 + \ln a^3.$$ **(2 marks)**

b Show that

$$\sum_{r=1}^{20} \ln [7(3^r)] = 10(2 \ln 7 + 21 \ln 3).$$ **(5 marks)**

8   Solve the simultaneous equations

$$3x + \ln y - 12 = 0$$
$$x + \ln y^2 + 1 = 0$$

(4 marks)

9   Solve the equation

$$5^{2x} + 3(5^x) - 10 = 0,$$

giving any answers correct to an appropriate degree of accuracy.   (5 marks)

10   A curve has the equation

$$y = 12 - e^{2x}.$$

The points $P\,(\ln 2, p)$ and $Q\,(q, {}^-4)$ lie on the curve.

a   Find the values of p and q.   (5 marks)

b   Find the coordinates of the midpoint of PQ.   (2 marks)

11   Giving your answers correct to an appropriate degree of accuracy, solve the equations

a $2^x = 150$,   (3 marks)

b $\lg\,(25 - x) = 2 - \lg x$.   (5 marks)

12   Given that

$$\ln y = 2 \ln x + 3,$$

show that $y = kx^2$ and find the value of k in terms of e.   (4 marks)

13

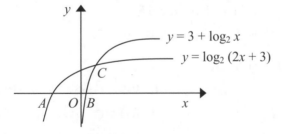

The diagram shows the curves

$$y = \log_2\,(2x + 3), \quad x > -\tfrac{3}{2}, \text{ and}$$
$$y = 3 + \log_2 x, \quad x > 0,$$

which cross the x-axis at the points A and B respectively.

a   Find the coordinates of the points A and B.   (4 marks)

The two curves intersect at the point C.

b   Show that the point C has coordinates $(\tfrac{1}{2}, 2)$.   (5 marks)

Functions and Inverses

Exercise 8S   Skills Practice

IN THIS EXERCISE THE DOMAIN IS THE SET OF REAL NUMBERS RESTRICTED AS INDICATED

1 $f(x) \equiv 2x + 1$ $\qquad$ $g(x) \equiv 4 - x^2$ $\qquad$ $h(x) \equiv \frac{3}{x} - 2$

Find the value of

a $f(2)$ $\qquad$ **b** $f(8)$ $\qquad$ **c** $f(\frac{7}{2})$ $\qquad$ **d** $f(^-6)$ $\qquad$ **e** $g(3)$ $\qquad$ **f** $g(^-2)$

g $g(6)$ $\qquad$ **h** $g(^-\frac{3}{2})$ $\qquad$ **i** $h(1)$ $\qquad$ **j** $h(^-9)$ $\qquad$ **k** $h(\frac{1}{4})$ $\qquad$ **l** $h(\frac{3}{5})$

2 Sketch $y = f(x)$ and state the range of f in each case.

a $f(x) \equiv 3x + 1$ $\qquad\qquad\qquad$ **b** $f(x) \equiv x^2 - 2$

c $f(x) \equiv 2x - 5, \ 0 < x < 4$ $\qquad\qquad$ **d** $f(x) \equiv e^x$

e $f(x) \equiv 5 - x^2, \ x > 1$ $\qquad\qquad$ **f** $f(x) \equiv \frac{1}{x}, \ \frac{1}{2} \le x \le 8$

g $f(x) \equiv 3x^3, \ ^-2 < x < 2$ $\qquad\qquad$ **h** $f(x) \equiv 4 - \frac{1}{3}x, \ ^-6 \le x < 9$

3 Find the domain of each function given its range.

a $f : x \to x + 5, \ 5 < f(x) < 10$ $\qquad$ **b** $f : x \to 3 - 2x, \ ^-5 \le f(x) \le 7$

c $f : x \to \frac{4}{x}, \ \frac{1}{2} \le f(x) \le 2$ $\qquad\qquad$ **d** $f : x \to 2x^3 + 1, \ ^-1 < f(x) \le 1$

4 **a** Express $x^2 + 6x + 2$ in the form $a(x + b)^2 + c$.

$\quad$ **b** State the range of the function $f(x) \equiv x^2 + 6x + 2$.

5 Find the range of f in each case.

a $f(x) \equiv x^2 - 4x + 5$ $\qquad\qquad$ **b** $f(x) \equiv x^2 + 8x + 2, \ x > 0$

c $f(x) \equiv 2 + 6x - x^2$ $\qquad\qquad$ **d** $f(x) \equiv x^2 - 10x + 15, \ 0 \le x \le 6$

e $f(x) \equiv 2x^2 - 4x + 3$ $\qquad\qquad$ **f** $f(x) \equiv x^2 + 3x + 1, \ ^-3 < x < 2$

6 $f(x) \equiv 2x - 4$ $\qquad$ $g(x) \equiv 4 - x^2$ $\qquad$ $h(x) \equiv \frac{3}{x} + 1, \ x \ne 0$

Solve

a $f(x) = 8$ $\qquad\qquad$ **b** $f(x) = ^-7$ $\qquad\qquad$ **c** $g(x) = 0$

d $h(x) = 6$ $\qquad\qquad$ **e** $f(x) = h(x)$ $\qquad\qquad$ **f** $f(x) - 2g(x) = 0$

7 Find $f^{-1}(x)$ in each case, stating its domain clearly.

a $f : x \to 2x - 1$ $\qquad\qquad\qquad$ **b** $f : x \to \frac{x+1}{4}$

c $f : x \to \frac{2}{x}, \ x \ne 0$ $\qquad\qquad\qquad$ **d** $f : x \to 7 + 2x, \ 0 < x < 5$

8   In each case sketch $y = f(x)$ and $y = f^{-1}(x)$ on the same set of coordinate axes.

   a $f(x) \equiv 10 - 3x$

   b $f(x) \equiv \frac{1}{2}x + 3, \ ^-1 \leq x \leq 6$

   c $f(x) \equiv \ln x, \ x > 0$

   d $f(x) \equiv x^2, \ x < 0$

   e $f(x) \equiv 4x^{\frac{1}{2}}, \ x \geq 0$

   f $f(x) \equiv x^2 - 4x + 4, \ x > 2$

9   Find and simplify an expression for $f^{-1}(x)$ in each case.

   a $f : x \rightarrow e^{x+1}$

   b $f : x \rightarrow \frac{1}{x+2}, \ x \neq ^-2$

   c $f : x \rightarrow 3 - \frac{4}{x}, \ x \neq 0$

   d $f : x \rightarrow \log_3 (2x - 1), \ x > \frac{1}{2}$

   e $f : x \rightarrow \frac{x+1}{x-3}, \ x \neq 3$

   f $f : x \rightarrow \frac{2x-1}{5-x}, \ x \neq 5$

10 **a** Express $x^2 - 2x + 3$ in the form $a(x + b)^2 + c$.

   b Given that $f(x) \equiv x^2 - 2x + 3, \ x > 1$, define $f^{-1}(x)$, stating its domain clearly.

11 Find $f^{-1}(x)$ in each case, stating its domain clearly.

   a $f(x) \equiv x^2 + 4x + 1, \ x \leq ^-2$

   b $f(x) \equiv x^2 - 12x + 20, \ x < 3$

   c $f(x) \equiv 2 - 2x - x^2, \ x > ^-1$

   d $f(x) \equiv x^2 + 3x - 4, \ x \geq \frac{3}{2}$

   e $f(x) \equiv 3x^2 - 12x, \ x > 2$

   f $f(x) \equiv x^2 - x + 1, \ 1 \leq x \leq 3$

12 $f(x) \equiv 4 - e^{2x}$ $g(x) \equiv \ln (2 - 3x)$

   Find, in exact form, the values of x for which

   a $f(x) = 3$ **b** $g(x) = 4$ **c** $f^{-1}(x) = ^-1$ **d** $g^{-1}(x) = 0.5$

13 In each case state whether the function is odd, even or neither.

   a $f(x) \equiv 3x$

   b $f(x) \equiv x + 2$

   c $f(x) \equiv x^2 - 4$

   d $f(x) \equiv \cos x$

   e $f(x) \equiv e^x$

   f $f(x) \equiv 2x^3$

14 $f(x)$ is an even function and defined for all real values of x.

   Given that for $x \geq 0, \ f(x) \equiv 2x - 3$,

   a sketch $y = f(x)$,

   b find the set of values of x for which $f(x) > 0$.

15 $g(x)$ is an odd function and defined for all real values of x.

   Given that for $x \geq 0, \ g(x) \equiv x^2 - 2x$,

   a sketch $y = g(x)$,

   b state the coordinates of any points where the curve meets the coordinate axes.

Exercise 8E   Exam Practice

1   The function f is defined by
$$f : x \rightarrow \log_2 x, \ x \in \mathbb{R}, \ x > 0.$$

   a Evaluate f(32).   **(1 mark)**

   b Solve the equation
   $$f(4^{x-2}) = 1 - 3x.$$ **(4 marks)**

2   The function f is defined by
$$f(x) \equiv \tfrac{x}{2-x}, \ x \in \mathbb{R}, \ x < 2.$$

   a Express f($\sqrt{2}$) in the form $A + B\sqrt{2}$.   **(3 marks)**

   b Find an expression for $f^{-1}(x)$ and state its range.   **(4 marks)**

3   The function f is an odd function defined for all real values of x.

   Given that $f(x) \equiv 2x, \qquad 0 \le x \le 1$, and
   $$f(x) \equiv 3 - x^2, \qquad x > 1,$$

   a sketch the graph of $y = f(x)$ in the interval $[^-2, 2]$,   **(4 marks)**

   b state, with a reason, whether or not $f^{-1}(x)$ exists.   **(2 marks)**

4   The function f is defined by
$$f : x \rightarrow \tfrac{x-2}{3x}, \ x \in \mathbb{R}, \ x \neq 0.$$

   a Define $f^{-1}(x)$, stating its domain clearly.   **(4 marks)**

   b Prove that there are no real values of x for which
   $$f(x) = f^{-1}(x).$$ **(4 marks)**

5 $$f(x) \equiv x^2 - 6x + 7, \ x \in \mathbb{R}, \ x < 1.$$

   a Express f(x) in the form $A(x + B)^2 + C$.   **(3 marks)**

   b Sketch the curves $y = f(x)$ and $y = f^{-1}(x)$ on the same set of
   coordinate axes.   **(4 marks)**

   c Define $f^{-1}(x)$, stating its domain clearly.   **(5 marks)**

6   The function f is given by
$$f(x) \equiv 2e^x - 1, \ x \in \mathbb{R}.$$

   a Find an expression for $f^{-1}(x)$.   **(3 marks)**

   The function g is given by
   $$g(x) \equiv 2x^2 + 4x + 1, \ x \in \mathbb{R}, \ x \le k.$$

   b Find the maximum value of k for which $g^{-1}(x)$ exists.   **(4 marks)**

Composite Functions

Exercise 9S   Skills Practice

IN THIS EXERCISE THE DOMAIN IS THE SET OF REAL NUMBERS RESTRICTED AS INDICATED

1 $f(x) \equiv x + 5$ $g(x) \equiv 4x - 1$ $h(x) \equiv x^2 + 7$

Find the value of

a fg(2)   b gf(2)   c gg(3)

d fh(¯3)   e hg($\frac{3}{2}$)   f gh(¯6)

2 $f : x \rightarrow x + 3$ $g : x \rightarrow 6 - 4x$ $h : x \rightarrow 2x^2 - 1$

Find and simplify an expression for each composite function.

a fg   b gf   c gh

d hf   e ggg   f fhg

3 $f(x) \equiv 3x - 4$ $g(x) \equiv 2x^2 - 8$ $h(x) \equiv 1 + \frac{2}{x}$, $x \neq 0$

Solve

a ff(x) = 20   b fg(x) = 2   c fh(x) = ¯7

d hf(x) = 5   e hh(x) = 5   f gf(x) = 10

4 $f(x) \equiv 5 - e^x$ $g(x) \equiv x^2 - 4$ $h(x) \equiv \ln(3x - 1)$, $x > \frac{1}{3}$

Find the value of

a fg(1)   b ff^{-1}(3)   c ff(¯2)

d hf(ln 4)   e gh(4.2)   f fgh(4)

5 $f(x) \equiv e^{\frac{2}{3}x}$ $g(x) \equiv 2e^x - 1$ $h(x) \equiv 3 \ln x$, $x > 0$

Find and simplify an expression for each composite function.

a hf   b fh   c gh

6 $f : x \rightarrow 2 + \frac{1}{x}$, $x \neq 0$ $g : x \rightarrow \frac{x}{3-x}$, $x \neq 3$

Find and simplify an expression for each composite function.

a fg   b gf   c fff

7 $f(x) \equiv \frac{x+2}{x}$, $x \neq 0$ $g(x) \equiv \frac{x-1}{x+4}$, $x \neq ^-4$

Solve

a fg(x) = 2   b gf(x) = 0.25   c gf(x) = g(x)

Exercise 9E   Exam Practice

1   The functions f and g are given by
$$f : x \rightarrow kx - 3, \ x \in \mathbb{R},$$
$$g : x \rightarrow x + 2k, \ x \in \mathbb{R}.$$

    a Find an expression for fg in terms of k.   **(2 marks)**

    b Given that fg(5) = 0, find the two possible values of k.   **(4 marks)**

2   The function f is defined by
$$f(x) \equiv \frac{x}{2x-3}, \ x \in \mathbb{R}, \ x \neq \frac{3}{2}.$$

    a Define $f^{-1}(x)$ and state its domain.   **(4 marks)**

    b Show that $ff(x) \equiv \frac{x}{9-4x}$.   **(3 marks)**

3   The functions f and g are defined as follows:
$$f : x \rightarrow 3 - 2x^2, \ x \in \mathbb{R},$$
$$g : x \rightarrow e^{-\frac{1}{2}x}, \ x \in \mathbb{R}.$$

    a State the range of f.   **(1 mark)**

    b Find and simplify an expression for fg.   **(3 marks)**

    c Solve the equation
$$fg(x) = \frac{5}{2}$$

    giving your answer in the form $k \ln 2$.   **(4 marks)**

4   The functions f and g are given by
$$f(x) \equiv 2x - 1, \ x \in \mathbb{R},$$
$$g(x) \equiv x^2 + 8, \ x \in \mathbb{R}.$$

    a Define fg and state its range.   **(3 marks)**

    b Solve the equation
$$fg(x) = gf(x).$$ **(5 marks)**

5   The functions f and g are defined by
$$f : x \rightarrow \frac{x+3}{2x}, \ x \in \mathbb{R}, \ x \neq 0.$$
$$g : x \rightarrow \frac{x-1}{1-4x}, \ x \in \mathbb{R}, \ x \neq \frac{1}{4}.$$

    a Find the inverse function $f^{-1}(x)$ and state its domain.   **(4 marks)**

    b Solve the equation
$$f(x) = f^{-1}(x).$$ **(4 marks)**

    c Evaluate $fg(\frac{1}{3})$.   **(3 marks)**

    d Show that $gf(x) \equiv \frac{x-3}{2(x+6)}$.   **(4 marks)**

Transformations of Functions

Exercise 10S   Skills Practice

1 Describe how the graph of $y = f(x)$ is transformed to give the graph of

    a $y = f(x + 2)$ **b** $y = 3f(x)$ **c** $y = 6 + f(x)$

    d $y = {}^-f(x)$ **e** $y = f(4x)$ **f** $y = f({}^-x)$

2 Given that $f(x) \equiv x^2$, $x \in \mathbb{R}$, sketch each of the following graphs labelling the coordinates of the turning point in each case.

    a $y = f(x) + 2$ **b** $y = \frac{1}{3} f(x)$ **c** $y = f(5x)$

    d $y = 3 - f(x)$ **e** $y = f(x - 1)$ **f** $y = 2f(x) - 4$

3 Given that $f(x) \equiv 2x - 3$, $x \in \mathbb{R}$, sketch each of the following graphs labelling the coordinates of any points where each graph meets the coordinate axes.

    a $y = f(3x)$ **b** $y = f(x) + 3$ **c** $y = f(x - 1)$

    d $y = 4f(x)$ **e** $y = f({}^-2x)$ **f** $y = 5 + 2f(x)$

4

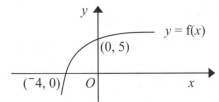

The diagram shows the curve $y = f(x)$ which meets the coordinate axes at the points $({}^-4, 0)$ and $(0, 5)$. Sketch each of the following graphs labelling the coordinates of any points where each curve meets the coordinate axes.

    a $y = 2f(x)$ **b** $y = f(x) - 5$ **c** $y = f(3x)$

    d $y = f(x - 4)$ **e** $y = f({}^-\frac{1}{2} x)$ **f** $y = {}^-\frac{3}{2} f(x)$

5

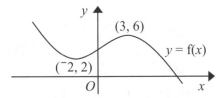

The diagram shows the curve $y = f(x)$ which is stationary at the points $({}^-2, 2)$ and $(3, 6)$. Sketch each of the following graphs labelling the coordinates of any stationary points on each curve.

    a $y = 3 + f(x)$ **b** $y = f(2x)$ **c** $y = \frac{2}{3} f(x)$

    d $y = f(x + 5)$ **e** $y = 2f(x) - 3$ **f** $y = f(1 - x)$

6   Describe, in order, transformations of the graph $y = f(x)$ that will produce the graph of

a $y = 3 + f(x + 1)$ b $y = 4f(x - 5)$ c $y = 2 - f(x)$

d $y = 6f(2x)$ e $y = f(3x - 3)$ f $y = f(\frac{1}{2}x + 2)$

7   a   Sketch the graph of $y = f(x)$ when $f(x) \equiv \frac{1}{x}$, $x \in \mathbb{R}$, $x \neq 0$.

b   By considering $f(x - 2)$, sketch the graph of $y = \frac{1}{x-2}$, $x \neq 2$.

8   By considering transformations of standard functions, sketch each of the following graphs.

a $y = (x + 3)^2$ b $y = e^x - 1$ c $y = \ln(3x)$, $x > 0$.

d $y = 1 + \frac{4}{x}$, $x \neq 0$ e $y = 2(x - 1)^3$ f $y = 5 - e^{2x}$

g $y = (x + 2)^{\frac{1}{2}}$, $x > ^{-}2$ h $y = \ln(3 - x)$, $x < 3$ i $y = (4 - x)^{-1}$, $x \neq 4$

9   Sketch each graph, labelling the coordinates of any points where each graph meets the coordinate axes.

a $y = |3x + 1|$ b $y = |2x - 5|$ c $y = |4 - x|$

d $y = |x^2 - 4|$ e $y = |x| + 3$ f $y = 2 - |x|$

10   a   Sketch the graphs of $y = |2x + 1|$ and $y = x + 3$ on the same set of coordinate axes.

b   Find the coordinates of the points where the two graphs intersect.

11   Solve

a $|3x - 2| = |x|$ b $|x + 1| = 2x + 5$ c $|4x + 3| = |x|$

d $|x - 3| = |2x + 3|$ e $|x| + 2 = \frac{1}{2}x + 4$ f $|2x - 1| = 3 - |x|$

12   Sketch $y = |f(x)|$ in each case.

a $f(x) \equiv 5 - \frac{1}{4}x$, $x \in \mathbb{R}$.   b $f(x) \equiv 2 - x^2$, $x \in \mathbb{R}$.

c $f(x) \equiv \ln x$, $x \in \mathbb{R}$, $x > 0$.   d $f(x) \equiv \frac{1}{x-1}$, $x \in \mathbb{R}$, $x \neq 1$.

e $f(x) \equiv e^x - 2$, $x \in \mathbb{R}$.   f $f(x) \equiv 2 + \frac{3}{x}$, $x \in \mathbb{R}$, $x \neq 0$.

13   Sketch $y = f(|x|)$ in each case.

a $f(x) \equiv x - 2$, $x \in \mathbb{R}$.   b $f(x) \equiv 4x + 1$, $x \in \mathbb{R}$.

c $f(x) \equiv \frac{1}{3x}$, $x \in \mathbb{R}$, $x \neq 0$.   d $f(x) \equiv e^x$, $x \in \mathbb{R}$.

e $f(x) \equiv x^2 - 3x$, $x \in \mathbb{R}$.   f $f(x) \equiv 2 + 4x - x^2$, $x \in \mathbb{R}$.

Exercise 10E   Exam Practice

1 **a** Sketch the graph of $y = |4x - 2|$ showing the coordinates of any
points where the graph meets the coordinate axes.   **(3 marks)**

    b Solve the equation
$$|4x - 2| = 2x + 1.$$ **(4 marks)**

2

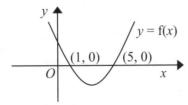

The diagram shows the curve $y = f(x)$ which meets the x-axis at the
points with coordinates $(1, 0)$ and $(5, 0)$.

Showing the coordinates of any points where each curve meets the
x-axis, sketch on separate diagrams graphs of

    a $y = f(x + 3)$,   **(3 marks)**

    b $y = |2f(x)|$,   **(3 marks)**

    c $y = f(|x|)$.   **(3 marks)**

3 **a** Given that $f(x) \equiv 3 + mx - x^2$, $x \in \mathbb{R}$, find the value of m such
that for all values of x,
$$f(|x|) = f(x).$$ **(2 marks)**

    b Given that $g(x) \equiv x^2 + 5x + n$, $x \in \mathbb{R}$, find the set of values of n
such that for all values of x,
$$|g(x)| = g(x).$$ **(4 marks)**

4

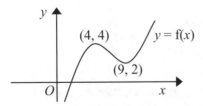

The diagram shows the curve $y = f(x)$. The curve has two stationary
points with coordinates $(4, 4)$ and $(9, 2)$.

Showing the coordinates of any stationary points sketch on separate
diagrams graphs of

    a $y = f(3x)$,   **(2 marks)**

    b $y = 2f(x) - 4$,   **(3 marks)**

    c $y = f(2x + 1)$.   **(4 marks)**

Functions Review

Exercise 11E   Exam Practice

1   The functions f and g are given by

$$f(x) \equiv 5 - 2x, \ x \in \mathbb{R},$$
$$g(x) \equiv \tfrac{1}{2}x + 3, \ x \in \mathbb{R}.$$

a Evaluate $fg(^-\tfrac{4}{3})$.   **(2 marks)**

b Solve the equation

$$gf(x) = 2.$$ **(4 marks)**

2   The function f is defined by

$$f : x \to 2 + \tfrac{3}{x}, \ x \in \mathbb{R}, \ x \neq 0.$$

a Define $f^{-1}(x)$ and state its domain.   **(4 marks)**

b Sketch the graph of $y = f^{-1}(x)$ labelling the coordinates of any
points where the curve meets the coordinate axes and the
equation of any asymptotes.   **(4 marks)**

3   **a** Sketch on the same diagram the graphs of $y = |4x - 2|$ and
$y = |2x|$ showing the coordinates of any points where each
graph meets the coordinate axes.   **(4 marks)**

b Find the coordinates of the points where the two graphs intersect. **(4 marks)**

4

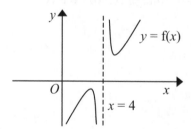

The diagram shows the curve $y = f(x)$ which is stationary at the
points with coordinates $(3, {}^-2)$ and $(5, 4)$. The curve has an
asymptote with the equation $x = 4$.

Showing the coordinates of any stationary points and the equation
of any asymptotes, sketch on separate diagrams graphs of

a $y = f(x - 3)$,   **(3 marks)**

b $y = |f(x)|$,   **(3 marks)**

c $y = \tfrac{1}{2}f(x)$.   **(3 marks)**

5   The functions f and g are given by

$$f(x) \equiv 6 - 3^x, \ x \in \mathbb{R},$$
$$g(x) \equiv 2 \log_3 x, \ x \in \mathbb{R}, \ x > 0.$$

a   Find and simplify an expression for fg.   **(3 marks)**

b   Find an expression for $f^{-1}(x)$.   **(3 marks)**

c   Solve the equation

$$g(x) = f^{-1}(x).$$ **(3 marks)**

6   a   Sketch the graph of $y = \left| 3 - \frac{1}{2} x \right|$ showing the coordinates of any points where the graph meets the coordinate axes.   **(3 marks)**

b   Find the set of values of x for which

$$\left| 3 - \frac{1}{2} x \right| < 2.$$ **(4 marks)**

7   The functions f and g are given by

$$f : x \rightarrow 4x + 9, \ x \in \mathbb{R},$$
$$g : x \rightarrow x(x - 3), \ x \in \mathbb{R}.$$

a   Find the values of a and b such that

$$fg(x) \equiv (ax + b)^2.$$ **(3 marks)**

b   Sketch the curve $y = fg(|x|)$, labelling the coordinates of any points where it meets the coordinate axes.   **(5 marks)**

8

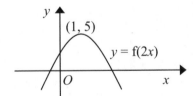

The diagram shows the curve $y = f(2x)$ which has a maximum at the point with coordinates $(1, 5)$

Showing the coordinates of the stationary point in each case, sketch on separate diagrams graphs of

a $y = 3 - f(2x)$,   **(4 marks)**

b $y = f(x - 1)$.   **(4 marks)**

9   The functions f and g are defined by

$$f : x \rightarrow x^2 - x, \ x \in \mathbb{R}.$$
$$g : x \rightarrow 4 - 2^x, \ x \in \mathbb{R}.$$

a   Find and simplify an expression for fg.   **(3 marks)**

b   Giving any answers correct to an appropriate degree of accuracy, solve the equation

$$fg(x) = 0.$$ **(5 marks)**

10 **a** Given that $k > 0$, sketch on the same set of coordinate axes the graphs of $y = 2k - x$ and $y = |3x + k|$, labelling the coordinates of any points where each graph meets the coordinate axes.   **(5 marks)**

  b Find in terms of k, where $k > 0$, the values of x for which
$$|3x + k| = 2k - x.$$
    (5 marks)

11 The functions f and g are given by
$$f(x) \equiv e^{2x}, \ x \in \mathbb{R},$$
$$g(x) \equiv 5 - x^2, \ x \in \mathbb{R}.$$

  a State the range of f.   **(1 mark)**

  b Find the value of fg(3) correct to 3 significant figures.   **(2 marks)**

  c Solve the equation
$$gf(x) = 1,$$
giving your answer in the form $k \ln 2$.   **(5 marks)**

12 The function f is given by
$$f(x) \equiv \tfrac{x}{3 - 2x}, \ x \in \mathbb{R}, \ x \neq \tfrac{3}{2}.$$

  a Find $f(\sqrt{2})$ in the form $a + b\sqrt{2}$.   **(3 marks)**

  b Define $f^{-1}(x)$ and state its domain.   **(4 marks)**

13 Solve the equation
$$|3x - 5| = 6 - |x|.$$
    (6 marks)

14 The function f is given by
$$f : x \rightarrow \ln(4x - 1), \ x \in \mathbb{R}, \ x > \tfrac{1}{4}.$$

  a Find an expression for $f^{-1}(x)$.   **(3 marks)**

  b State the range of $f^{-1}(x)$.   **(1 mark)**

  The function g is given by
$$g : x \rightarrow \ln(2x), \ x \in \mathbb{R}, \ x > 0.$$

  c Define the function h such that
$$f(x) \equiv gh(x).$$
    (2 marks)

15 The function f is given by
$$f(x) \equiv x^2 - 6x + 2, \ x \in \mathbb{R}, \ x \geq 3.$$

  a Express $f(x)$ in the form $A(x + B)^2 + C$.   **(3 marks)**

  b Sketch the curves $y = f(x)$ and $y = f^{-1}(x)$ on the same set of coordinate axes.   **(4 marks)**

  c Define $f^{-1}(x)$, stating its domain clearly.   **(5 marks)**

Trigonometric Ratios and Graphs

Exercise 12S	Skills Practice

1   Find in exact form, with a rational denominator, the value of

   a   cosec 30°   b   cot 60°   c   sec 225°   d   cosec (⁻120°)

2   Find in exact form, with a rational denominator, the value of

   a $\sec \frac{\pi}{4}$ b $\csc \frac{4\pi}{3}$ c $\cot(-\frac{5\pi}{6})$ d $\sec \frac{8\pi}{3}$

3   Given that $\sin x = \frac{3}{5}$, $0 < x < 90°$, find, without using a calculator, the value of

   a   cos x   b   sec x   c   cosec x   d   cot x

4   Sketch each graph in the interval ⁻180° < x < 180° showing the coordinates of
     any turning points and the equations of any asymptotes.

   a $y = \csc x$ b $y = 2\sec x$ c $y = \cot 2x$

   d $y = \sec(x + 30°)$ e $y = \cot(x - 45°)$ f $y = 3\csc 2x$

   g $y = -\frac{1}{2}\cot(x + 120°)$ h $y = 1 + \csc(\frac{1}{2}x)$ i $y = 3 - 2\sec x$

5   Find, in terms of π, the values of θ in the interval ⁻$\pi \le \theta \le \pi$ for which

   a $\csc \theta = 2$ b $\cot(\theta + \frac{\pi}{3}) = \sqrt{3}$ c $\sec 3\theta = \sqrt{2}$

   d $\sqrt{3}\cot(\frac{1}{2}\theta) = 1$ e $\sec(2\theta - \frac{2\pi}{3}) = ^-1$ f $3\csc^2\theta - 4 = 0$

6   Solve each equation for x in the interval $0 \le x \le 360°$.
     Give non-exact answers correct to 1 dp.

   a $\cot x = 1$ b $\csc(x + 30°) = 4.6$ c $\sec(2x - 40°) + 9.15 = 0$

   d $\sec x - 2\tan x = 0$ e $3\csc x = 2\sec x$ f $3\cot x - 8\sec x = 0$

7   Sketch the graph of each inverse trigonometric function indicating clearly the
     domain and range in each case.

   a $y = \arcsin x$ b $y = \arccos x$ c $y = \arctan x$

8   Find in radians, in terms of π, the value of

   a $\arcsin \frac{1}{2}$ b $\arccos \frac{\sqrt{3}}{2}$ c $\arctan(^-1)$

   d $\arccos \frac{1}{\sqrt{2}}$ e $\arctan \sqrt{3}$ f $\arcsin(-\frac{\sqrt{3}}{2})$

9   Solve each equation giving non-exact answers correct to 3 sf.

   a $\arccos x = \frac{\pi}{6}$ b $\arctan x = 0.685$ c $4\arcsin x + 3 = 0$

Exercise 12E   Exam Practice

1   Find the values of x in the interval $0 \le x \le 2\pi$ for which

$$3\tan x - \cot x = 0,$$

giving your answers in terms of π.   **(5 marks)**

2 $$f(x) \equiv \frac{\pi}{2} + \arcsin x, \quad x \in \mathbb{R}, \quad ^{-}1 \le x \le 1.$$

a   Find the value of $f(\frac{1}{2})$ in terms of π.   **(2 marks)**

b   Sketch the graph of $y = f(x)$ and state the range of f.   **(4 marks)**

c   Find, in exact form, the value of x for which $f(x) = \frac{\pi}{4}$.   **(3 marks)**

3

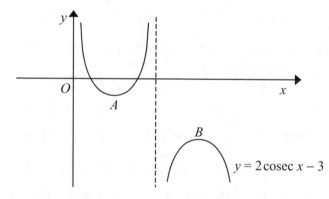

The diagram shows the curve $y = 2\operatorname{cosec} x - 3$ for x in the interval $0 < x < 360°$.

a   Find the coordinates of the minimum point, A, and the maximum point, B, on the curve.   **(3 marks)**

b   Find, correct to 1 decimal place, the x-coordinates of the points where the curve crosses the x-axis.   **(5 marks)**

4   Find the values of x in the interval $^{-}180° \le x \le 180°$ for which

$$\sec x + 4\cos x = 5,$$

giving your answers correct to an appropriate degree of accuracy.   **(7 marks)**

5 $$f(x) \equiv \tfrac{1}{2}\sec(x + \tfrac{\pi}{3}), \quad x \in \mathbb{R}.$$

a   Sketch the graph of $y = f(x)$ in the interval $[0, 2\pi]$ labelling the coordinates of any turning points.   **(5 marks)**

b   Solve the equation

$$f(x) + 1 = 0,$$

for x in the interval $[0, 2\pi]$, giving your answers in terms of π.   **(5 marks)**

Trigonometric Identities I

Exercise 13S   Skills Practice

1   Use the identity $\sin^2 x + \cos^2 x \equiv 1$ to prove the identities

    a $1 + \tan^2 x \equiv \sec^2 x$ **b** $1 + \cot^2 x \equiv \mathrm{cosec}^2 x$

2   Solve each equation for x in the interval $0 \le x \le 360°$.
    Give non-exact answers correct to 1 dp.

    a $4\tan^2 x = \sec^2 x$ **b** $\sec^2 x - 4\tan x + 3 = 0$

    c $\cot^2 x + \mathrm{cosec}\, x = 1$ **d** $\tan^2 x - 2\sec x = 7$

    e $2\mathrm{cosec}^2 x = 5(1 - \cot x)$ **f** $\cot^2 x - 8 \sin x + 1 = 0$

    g $\tan^2 2x - 3\sec 2x + 3 = 0$ **h** $\tan^2 x + 9 = 9\mathrm{cosec}^2 x$

3   Prove the following identities:

    a $\tan^2 x - \cot^2 x \equiv \sec^2 x - \mathrm{cosec}^2 x$ **b** $(\cot x + 1)^2 \equiv \mathrm{cosec}^2 x + 2 \cot x$

    c $\sec^2 x + \mathrm{cosec}^2 x \equiv \sec^2 x \, \mathrm{cosec}^2 x$ **d** $\sec x - \cos x \equiv \sin x \tan x$

    e $(\cos x - \sec x)^2 \equiv \tan^2 x - \sin^2 x$ **f** $\dfrac{\sin x}{\mathrm{cosec}\, x - \cot x} \equiv 1 + \cos x$

    g $\mathrm{cosec}^2 x \equiv \dfrac{\sec x}{\sec x - \cos x}$ **h** $\cot^2 x - \cos^2 x \equiv \cos^2 x \cot^2 x$

4   Use the identities for $\sin (A + B)$ and $\cos (A + B)$ to obtain the identities for

    a $\sin(A - B)$ **b** $\cos(A - B)$ **c** $\tan(A + B)$ **d** $\tan(A - B)$

5   Use the fact that $\sin 15° = \sin (45° - 30°)$ to show that $\sin 15° = \frac{1}{4}(\sqrt{6} - \sqrt{2})$.

6   Find in exact form, with a rational denominator, the value of

    a $\cos 15°$ **b** $\sec 15°$ **c** $\tan 75°$ **d** $\mathrm{cosec}\, 105°$

7   Simplify

    a $\sin A \cos 2A + \cos A \sin 2A$ **b** $\cos 3A \cos 5A + \sin 3A \sin 5A$

    c $2\sin A \sin 2B - 2\cos A \cos 2B$ **d** $\dfrac{\tan 4A + \tan B}{\tan 4A \tan B - 1}$

8   Find the maximum value that each expression can take and the smallest positive
    value of x, in degrees, for which this occurs.

    a $\sin x \cos 30° + \cos x \sin 30°$ **b** $\cos 2x \cos x - \sin 2x \sin x$

    c $2\cos x \sin 10° - 2\sin x \cos 10°$ **d** $3\cos 2x \cos 45° + 3\sin 2x \sin 45°$

9   Find the minimum value that each expression can take and the smallest positive value of θ, in radians in terms of π, for which this occurs.

    a $\cos\theta \cos\frac{\pi}{3} + \sin\theta \sin\frac{\pi}{3}$ **b** $2\sin 3\theta \cos\theta - 2\cos 3\theta \sin\theta$

    c $\sin 2\theta \sin\frac{\pi}{4} - \cos 2\theta \cos\frac{\pi}{4}$ **d** $\cos(\theta + \frac{\pi}{6})\sin\theta + \sin(\theta + \frac{\pi}{6})\cos\theta$

10   Given that $\cos x = \frac{3}{5}, 0 < x < 90°$, and that $\sin y = \frac{5}{13}, 90° < y < 180°$, find without using a calculator, the value of

    a $\cos y$ **b** $\sin(x+y)$ **c** $\tan(x-y)$ **d** $\sec(x+y)$

11   Solve each equation for θ in the interval $0 \le \theta \le 2\pi$.
Give non-exact answers correct to 2 dp.

    a $\sin\theta = \cos(\theta + \frac{\pi}{6})$ **b** $2\cos\theta + \sin(\theta - \frac{\pi}{4}) = 0$

    c $\tan(\theta + \frac{\pi}{4}) = 3\tan\theta + 2$ **d** $2\sin(\theta + \frac{\pi}{6}) = \cos(\theta + \frac{\pi}{3})$

12   Prove the following identities:

    a $\dfrac{\sin(A-B)}{\cos A \cos B} \equiv \tan A - \tan B$

    b $\cos(A+B)\cos(A-B) \equiv \cos^2 B - \sin^2 A$

    c $\sin(A+B) - \cos(A-B) \equiv (\sin A - \cos A)(\cos B - \sin B)$

13   Use the identities for $\sin(A+B)$ and $\cos(A+B)$ to prove that

    a $\sin 2A \equiv 2\sin A \cos A$ **b** $\cos 2A \equiv \cos^2 A - \sin^2 A$

14   Use the identity $\sin^2 x + \cos^2 x \equiv 1$ to prove that

    a $\cos 2A \equiv 2\cos^2 A - 1$ **b** $\cos 2A \equiv 1 - 2\sin^2 A$

15   Solve each equation for x in the interval $^-180° \le x \le 180°$.
Give non-exact answers correct to 1 dp.

    a $\sin 2x - \cos x = 0$ **b** $\cos 2x - 5\sin x = 3$

    c $\cos 2x + 3\cos x = 0$ **d** $2\sin 4x + 3\sin 2x = 0$

    e $\tan 2x = 2\cot x$ **f** $\operatorname{cosec} 2x - 2\cot 2x = 0$

16   Prove the following identities:

    a $(\cos x - \sin x)^2 \equiv 1 - \sin 2x$ **b** $\cos x \equiv 2\cos^2\frac{x}{2} - 1$

    c $2\cot 2x + \tan x \equiv \cot x$ **d** $\sin 3x \equiv 3\sin x - 4\sin^3 x$

    e $\operatorname{cosec} 2x - \cot 2x \equiv \tan x$ **f** $\cos 4x \equiv 8\cos^4 x - 8\cos^2 x + 1$

17   Using the half-angle formulae, prove that

    a $\dfrac{\cos x - 1}{\cos x + 1} \equiv {}^-\tan^2\frac{x}{2}$ **b** $\dfrac{\cos x + 1}{\sin x} \equiv \cot\frac{x}{2}$

Exercise 13E   Exam Practice

1   **a**   Prove that
$$\cot x - \operatorname{cosec} 2x \equiv \cot 2x, \ x \neq 90n°, \ n \in \mathbb{Z}.$$
   (5 marks)

   b   Hence find the values of x in the interval $0 \leq x \leq 180°$ for which
$$\cot x - \operatorname{cosec} 2x = 4 - 3\tan 2x,$$
   giving your answers correct to an appropriate degree of accuracy.   **(6 marks)**

2   **a**   Use the identity
$$\cos(A + B) \equiv \cos A \cos B - \sin A \sin B,$$
   to prove the identity
$$\cos A \equiv 1 - 2\sin^2 \tfrac{A}{2}.$$
   (5 marks)

   b   Hence, find the values of θ in the interval $0 \leq \theta \leq 2\pi$ for which
$$\cos \theta + 2 = \sin \tfrac{\theta}{2}.$$
   (6 marks)

3

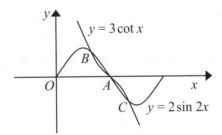

The diagram shows the graphs of $y = 2\sin 2x$ and $y = 3\cot x$ in the interval $(0, \pi)$.

The two graphs intersect at the points A, B and C.

   a   State the coordinates of the point A.   **(1 mark)**

   b   Find in exact form the coordinates of the points B and C.   **(8 marks)**

4   **a**   Find the values of x in the interval $0 \leq x \leq 2\pi$ for which
$$\sin 2x + \sqrt{2}\cos x = 0,$$
   giving your answers in terms of π.   **(5 marks)**

   b   Find the values of y in the interval $0 \leq y \leq 360°$ for which
$$\cot^2 y - 5\operatorname{cosec} y + 7 = 0,$$
   giving your answers correct to an appropriate degree of accuracy.   **(6 marks)**

5   Find, correct to 2 decimal places, all solutions of the equation

$$\sin(x + \tfrac{\pi}{3}) + \sqrt{3}\sin(x + \tfrac{\pi}{6}) = 0,$$

in the interval $0 \le x \le 2\pi$.   **(7 marks)**

6   **a**   Use the identity

$$\sin^2 x + \cos^2 x \equiv 1,$$

to prove the identity

$$1 + \tan^2 x \equiv \sec^2 x, \quad x \ne \frac{(2n+1)\pi}{2}, \quad n \in \mathbb{Z}.$$ **(2 marks)**

b   Show that there are no real values of x for which

$$6\tan^2 x - \sec x + 5 = 0.$$ **(5 marks)**

7   **a**   Use the identities

$$\sin(A + B) \equiv \sin A \cos B + \cos A \sin B, \text{ and}$$
$$\cos(A + B) \equiv \cos A \cos B - \sin A \sin B,$$

to prove the identity

$$\tan 2A \equiv \frac{2 \tan A}{1 - \tan^2 A}.$$ **(4 marks)**

b   Hence, use the fact that $\tan \frac{\pi}{4} = 1$ to find the value of $\tan \frac{\pi}{8}$ in the form $a\sqrt{2} + b$.   **(6 marks)**

8   **a**   Given that

$$\cos(x + 30°) - \sin(x - 45°) \equiv A\cos x + B\sin x,$$

show that $A = \frac{1}{2}(\sqrt{3} + \sqrt{2})$ and find the value of B.   **(5 marks)**

b   Hence find the values of x in the interval $0 \le x \le 360°$ for which

$$\cos(x + 30°) - \sin(x - 45°) = 0.$$ **(4 marks)**

9   **a**   Prove that

$$\cot x - \sin 2x \equiv \cot x \cos 2x, \quad x \ne n\pi, \quad n \in \mathbb{Z}.$$ **(5 marks)**

b   Find the values of x in the interval $0 \le x \le 360°$ for which

$$\cot x - \sin 2x = 0.$$ **(5 marks)**

10   **a**   Prove the identity

$$\cos^4 x - \sin^4 x \equiv \cos 2x.$$ **(3 marks)**

b   Given that

$$\sin(A + 2B) = \sin A,$$

show that

$$\tan A = \cot B.$$ **(6 marks)**

Trigonometric Identities II

1 In each case find the values of R and α where $R > 0$ and $0 < \alpha < 90°$.
   Give non-exact values of α correct to 1 dp.

   a $3 \cos x + 4 \sin x \equiv R \cos(x - \alpha)$ b $3 \cos x + 4 \sin x \equiv R \sin(x + \alpha)$

   c $7 \sin x + 24 \cos x \equiv R \cos(x - \alpha)$ d $\sin x - \cos x \equiv R \sin(x - \alpha)$

   e $2 \cos x - 3 \sin x \equiv R \cos(x + \alpha)$ f $4 \sin 2x + \cos 2x \equiv R \sin(2x + \alpha)$

2 Express each of the following in the form $R \cos(x + \alpha)$ where $|\alpha| < \frac{\pi}{2}$.

   a $\cos x + \sin x$ b $\sqrt{3} \cos x - \sin x$

   c $4 \sin x - 4 \cos x$ d $\sqrt{2} \cos x + \sqrt{6} \sin x$

3 By expressing each of the following in the form $y = R \sin(x + \alpha)$ or $R \cos(x + \alpha)$,
   where $R > 0$, and $|\alpha| < \frac{\pi}{2}$, sketch in the interval $[0, 2\pi]$ the graphs of

   a $y = 5 \sin x + 12 \cos x$ b $y = 3 \sin x - 3 \cos x$

   c $y = 6 \cos x - \sin x$ d $y = \frac{1}{2} \cos x + \frac{2}{3} \sin x$

4 Find the minimum value that each expression can take and the smallest positive
   value of x, in degrees correct to 1 dp, for which this occurs.

   a $6 \sin x + 8 \cos x$ b $\cos x - 3 \sin x$

   c $\sqrt{2} \sin x - 4 \cos x$ d $5 \cos 3x + 2 \sin 3x$

5 Solve each equation for x in the interval $^-180° \le x \le 180°$.
   Give non-exact answers correct to 1 dp.

   a $\sin x + \cos x = 1$ b $3 \cos x + 5 \sin x = 4$

   c $7 \sin x + 24 \cos x + 10 = 0$ d $\cos 2x = 2 \sin 2x - 1$

6 Solve each equation for θ in the interval $0 \le \theta \le 2\pi$.
   Give non-exact answers correct to 2 dp.

   a $3 \cos \theta - 4 \sin \theta = 5$ b $\sin \frac{\theta}{2} - \cos \frac{\theta}{2} = 1$

   c $24 \tan \theta + 10 = 13 \sec \theta$ d $\dfrac{\cos \theta - 1}{1 - 2 \sin \theta} = 3$

7 Find the coordinates of the turning points of each curve for x in the interval
   $0 \le x \le 360°$. Give non-exact answers correct to 1 dp.

   a $y = 15 \sin x + 8 \cos x$ b $y = \cos 2x - \sin 2x$

   c $y = \dfrac{1}{4 \sin x - 3 \cos x}$ d $y = \dfrac{12}{5 \cos x + 7 \sin x}$

8   Express each of the following as the sum or difference of trigonometric functions.

   a $2 \sin 3A \cos A$ **b** $2 \cos 2B \cos 5B$

   c $4 \sin 2A \sin 3A$ **d** $\cos 4A \sin A$

   e $2 \cos A \cos 2B$ **f** $\sin(3A + B) \cos(A - B)$

9   Express each of the following as the product of trigonometric functions.

   a $\cos 3A + \cos A$ **b** $\sin 6B - \sin 2B$

   c $3 \cos A - 3 \cos 5A$ **d** $\sin 2A + \sin 4B$

   e $\sin(3A - B) - \sin(A - B)$ **f** $\cos(A - 2B) + \cos(2A + 3B)$

10   Solve each equation for x in the interval $0 \le x \le 180°$.
         Give non-exact answers correct to 1 dp.

   a $\cos 4x = \cos 2x$ **b** $\sin 3x - \sin 2x = 0$

   c $\cos x + \cos \frac{x}{2} = 0$ **d** $\sin 3x + \sin(x - 60°) = 0$

   e $\cos 5x + \cos x = \cos 2x$ **f** $2 \sin 3x + 2 \sin x = 3 \cos x$

   g $2 \sin 3x \cos x = \sin 4x$ **h** $\cos 4x \cos x - \cos 3x = 0$

11   Prove the following identities:

   a $\sin 3x + \sin x \equiv 4 \sin x \cos^2 x$

   b $\cos x + \cos 2x + \cos 3x \equiv \cos 2x(2 \cos x + 1)$

   c $\dfrac{\sin 2A + \sin 2B}{\cos 2A + \cos 2B} \equiv \tan(A + B)$

Questions 12 and 13 require the use of all the P2 trigonometry work.

12   Solve each equation for x in the interval $0 \le x \le 360°$.
         Give non-exact answers correct to 1 dp.

   a $\tan^2 x - 4 \sec x + 4 = 0$ **b** $\sin(x + 30°) = \cos(x + 45°)$

   c $\sin 4x - \cos 2x = 0$ **d** $\sin 2x - \cos 2x + 1 = 0$

   e $\sqrt{3} \sec x + \csc x = 0$ **f** $\sin 4x = \sin 2x$

   g $4 \cos^2 x - \tan^2 x = 1$ **h** $\csc 2x + \sec x = 0$

13   Solve each equation for θ in the interval $0 \le \theta \le 2\pi$.
         Give non-exact answers correct to 2 dp.

   a $2 \cos \theta + 7 \sin \theta = 4$ **b** $\cos 2\theta = 4 - 7 \sin \theta$

   c $2\theta - \arcsin \frac{\sqrt{3}}{2} = \arctan(^-1)$ **d** $2 \tan \theta - 5 \csc \theta = 0$

   e $2 \sin(\theta - \frac{\pi}{4}) = 3 \cos \theta$ **f** $\cos 3\theta + \cos 2\theta = 0$

   g $2 \sin \theta + 3 \sin \frac{\theta}{2} = 0$ **h** $\sin 3\theta - \sin(\theta + \frac{\pi}{3}) = 0$

Exercise 14E   Exam Practice

1   **a** Solve, for x in the interval $^-180° \le x \le 180°$, the equation

$$\sin 2x = 5\cos x. \qquad \textbf{(4 marks)}$$

    b Solve, for θ in the interval $0 \le \theta \le \pi$, the equation

$$\sin 2\theta = \sin 5\theta,$$

       giving your answers in terms of π. **(6 marks)**

2                    $f(x) \equiv 4\sin x - 3\cos x.$

    a Express $f(x)$ in the form $R\sin(x - \alpha)$ where $R > 0$ and $0 < \alpha < 90°$. Give the value of α correct to 1 decimal place. **(5 marks)**

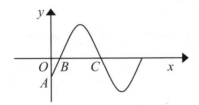

The diagram shows part of the curve $y = f(x)$ for $x \ge 0$.

    b Find the coordinates of the point A, where the curve crosses the y-axis. **(2 marks)**

    c Find the coordinates of the points B and C, where the curve crosses the x-axis. **(3 marks)**

3   **a** Use the identities

$$\sin(A + B) \equiv \sin A \cos B + \cos A \sin B, \text{ and}$$
$$\sin(A - B) \equiv \sin A \cos B - \cos A \sin B,$$

       to prove the identity

$$\sin A + \sin B \equiv 2\sin \frac{A+B}{2} \cos \frac{A-B}{2}. \qquad \textbf{(4 marks)}$$

    b Find, in terms of π, the values of θ in the interval $0 \le \theta \le \pi$ for which

$$\sin 5\theta + \sin 3\theta - \cos \theta = 0. \qquad \textbf{(6 marks)}$$

4                    $f(x) \equiv 5\sin 2x + 12\cos 2x.$

    a Find the values of R and α, where $R > 0$ and $0 < \alpha < 90°$, such that

$$f(x) \equiv R\cos(2x - \alpha). \qquad \textbf{(5 marks)}$$

    b Sketch the curve $y = f(x)$ in the interval $0 \le x \le 180°$ labelling the coordinates of any turning points. **(5 marks)**

5   **a**   Given that

$$2\sqrt{3}\cos\theta - 6\sin\theta \equiv R\cos(\theta + \alpha),$$

show that one possible value of α is $\frac{\pi}{3}$ and find the corresponding value of R in the form $k\sqrt{3}$.   **(5 marks)**

   b   Find, in terms of π, the values of θ in the interval $^-\pi \le \theta \le \pi$ for which

$$2\sqrt{3}\cos\theta - 6\sin\theta = 6.$$ **(5 marks)**

6   Prove the identities

   a $\sin x - \sin 3x + \sin 5x \equiv \sin 3x \, (2\cos 2x - 1),$ **(3 marks)**

   b $2\sin(x + \frac{\pi}{4})\cos(x + \frac{\pi}{4}) \equiv \cos 2x.$ **(5 marks)**

7   **a**   Find the values of x in the interval $0 \le x \le 360°$ for which

$$\cos x - \sqrt{3}\sin x = 1.$$ **(7 marks)**

   b   Given that

$$f(x) \equiv 3 + \cos x - \sqrt{3}\sin x,$$

find the minimum value of $f(x)$ and the smallest positive value of x for which $f(x)$ takes this value.   **(4 marks)**

8   **a**   Find the values of x in the interval $0 \le x \le 2\pi$ for which

$$\cos 3x + \cos x = 0,$$

giving your answers in terms of π.   **(5 marks)**

   b   Find the values of y in the interval $0 \le y \le 180°$ for which

$$\cos 4y + \cos 2y + \cos y = 0.$$ **(6 marks)**

9   **a**   Find the values of R and α, where $R > 0$ and $0 < \alpha < 90°$, for which

$$\frac{5}{8\cos x - 6\sin x} \equiv R\sec(x + \alpha),$$

giving the value of α correct to 1 decimal place.   **(6 marks)**

   b   Find the values of x in the interval $0 \le x \le 360°$ for which

$$\frac{5}{8\cos x - 6\sin x} = \frac{\sqrt{2}}{2},$$

giving your answers correct to 1 decimal place.   **(4 marks)**

Trigonometry Review

Exercise 15E	Exam Practice

1   a   Prove that

$$\csc^2 x + \sec^2 x \equiv 4\csc^2 2x, \ x \neq \frac{n\pi}{2}, \ n \in \mathbb{Z}. \qquad \textbf{(6 marks)}$$

   b   Hence find, in terms of π, the values of x in the interval $0 \leq x \leq \pi$
      for which

$$\csc^2 x + \sec^2 x = 8\cot^2 2x. \qquad \textbf{(6 marks)}$$

2   a   Find the values of R and α, where $R > 0$ and $0 < \alpha < \frac{\pi}{2}$,
      for which

$$\sin \theta + \sqrt{3} \cos \theta \equiv R \sin(\theta + \alpha). \qquad \textbf{(5 marks)}$$

   b   Hence find, the values of θ in the interval $0 \leq \theta \leq 2\pi$ for which

$$\sin \theta + \sqrt{3} \cos \theta \equiv 2\sin(\theta + \frac{\pi}{6}),$$

      giving your answers in terms of π.   **(5 marks)**

3

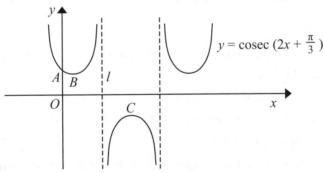

The diagram shows part of the curve $y = \csc(2x + \frac{\pi}{3})$.

Find in exact form the coordinates of

   a   the point A, where the curve crosses the y-axis,   **(2 marks)**

   b   the minimum point B,   **(3 marks)**

   c   the maximum point C.   **(2 marks)**

   d   State the equation of the asymptote l.   **(2 marks)**

4   a   Sketch on the same diagram the graphs of $y = \sin 4x$ and
      $y = \cot 6x$ in the interval $0 \leq x \leq 90°$.   **(5 marks)**

   b   State, with reasons, the number of solutions of the equation

$$\sin 4x = \cot 6x,$$

      which occur in the interval $0 \leq x \leq 360°$.   **(3 marks)**

5   **a**   For values of x in the interval $0 \le x \le 360°$, solve the equation

$$2\sin^2 x - 3\cos x = 0. \qquad \text{(4 marks)}$$

b   Hence find the values of y in the interval $0 \le y \le 180°$ for which

$$2\tan 2y - 3\operatorname{cosec} 2y = 0. \qquad \text{(4 marks)}$$

6 $$f(x) \equiv \arcsin x, \ x \in \mathbb{R}, \ ^-1 \le x \le 1.$$

a   Sketch the graph of $y = f(x)$.   **(2 marks)**

b   State the range of f.   **(1 mark)**

c   Find in exact form the value of x for which

$$3 f(x) - \pi = 0. \qquad \text{(3 marks)}$$

d   Find the value of k for which

$$\arcsin 1 = k \arctan 1. \qquad \text{(2 marks)}$$

7 $$f(x) \equiv \sin 2x + \cos 2x.$$

a   Express $f(x)$ in the form $R\cos(2x - \alpha)$ where $R > 0$ and $0 < \alpha < \frac{\pi}{2}$.

(5 marks)

b   Hence find, the values of x in the interval $0 \le x \le 2\pi$ for which $f(x) = 1$ giving your answers in terms of π.   **(4 marks)**

8   **a**   Use the identity

$$\cos(A + B) \equiv \cos A \cos B - \sin A \sin B,$$

to prove the identity

$$\cos 2A \equiv 2\cos^2 A - 1. \qquad \text{(3 marks)}$$

b   Hence, find the values of x in the interval $0 \le x \le 360°$ for which

$$3\cos 2x + 4\cos x + 1 = 0,$$

giving your answers correct to an appropriate degree of accuracy.   **(6 marks)**

9   **a**   Find the values of x in the interval $^-180° \le x \le 180°$ for which

$$\sec^2 x - 5\tan x + 3 = 0,$$

giving your answers correct to an appropriate degree of accuracy.   **(6 marks)**

b   Given that

$$\sqrt{2}\,\sin\left(y + \tfrac{\pi}{4}\right) = \cos\left(y - \tfrac{\pi}{6}\right),$$

show that

$$\tan y = \sqrt{3} - 2. \qquad \text{(5 marks)}$$

10 Prove the identities

    a $\operatorname{cosec} x - \sin x \equiv \cos x \cot x, \ x \neq n\pi, \ n \in \mathbb{Z}.$ **(4 marks)**

    b $\cot x + \tan x \equiv 2 \operatorname{cosec} 2x, \ x \neq \frac{n\pi}{2}, \ n \in \mathbb{Z}.$ **(5 marks)**

11

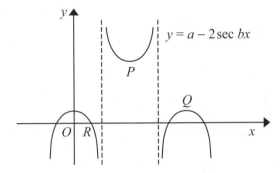

The diagram shows part of the curve with equation $y = a - 2\sec bx$.

Given that the minimum point P has coordinates ($\frac{\pi}{2}$, 5), find

    a   the values of a and b,   **(4 marks)**

    b   the coordinates of the maximum point Q,   **(2 marks)**

    c   the x-coordinate of the point R where the curve crosses the x-axis,
       correct to 3 significant figures.   **(4 marks)**

12   **a**   Find the values of x in the interval $0 \leq x \leq 180°$ for which

$$\cos 3x = \sin(3x + 60°).$$ **(6 marks)**

    b   Find the values of θ in the interval $0 \leq \theta \leq 2\pi$ for which

$$\sqrt{3}\sec \theta + 2 \tan \theta = 0,$$

       giving your answers in terms of π.   **(5 marks)**

13   **a**   Use the identities

$$\cos(A + B) \equiv \cos A \cos B - \sin A \sin B, \text{ and}$$
$$\cos(A - B) \equiv \cos A \cos B + \sin A \sin B,$$

       to prove the identity

$$\cos A - \cos B \equiv {}^{-}2\sin \frac{A+B}{2} \sin \frac{A-B}{2}.$$ **(4 marks)**

    b   Find the values of θ in the interval $0 \leq \theta \leq 2\pi$ for which

$$\cos 2\theta = \cos \frac{\theta}{2},$$

       giving your answers in terms of π.   **(6 marks)**

Differentiation

Exercise 16S	**Skills Practice**

1 Differentiate with respect to x.

  a e^x **b** $2e^x$ **c** $\frac{1}{3}e^x$ **d** $\ln x$ **e** $\ln 4x$ **f** $5\ln x$

2 Find $f'(x)$.

  a $f(x) \equiv x^2 + 2e^x$ **b** $f(x) \equiv \ln 3x - 1$ **c** $f(x) \equiv 4x + \frac{1}{2}e^x$

  d $f(x) \equiv 3\ln x - 2x^{\frac{5}{2}}$ **e** $f(x) \equiv 5e^x + 4\ln 2x$ **f** $f(x) \equiv x^3 + 3x - 6e^x$

3 Differentiate with respect to t.

  a $t - \frac{2}{3}e^t$ **b** $\ln 4t - t^{-2}$ **c** $6e^t + 2\ln\frac{t}{3}$

  d $\sqrt{t} + 2t + 5e^t$ **e** $6 - \frac{1}{2t} + 5\ln t$ **f** $\ln 3t + 2e^t + t^{\frac{3}{4}}$

4 Find $\dfrac{d^2 y}{dx^2}$ in each case.

  a $y = e^x - x^3$ **b** $y = 9x^{\frac{1}{3}} + 3\ln 2x$ **c** $y = 6\ln\left(\frac{1}{2}x\right) - 3e^x$

5 Find in each case any values of x for which $\dfrac{dy}{dx} = 0$.

  a $y = 3x - 2\ln 5x$ **b** $y = 4e^x - 2x$ **c** $y = x^2 - 7x + 3\ln x$

6 Find the coordinates and nature of any stationary points on each curve.

  a $y = 3x + 5 - e^x$ **b** $y = 6x - 3\ln 2x$ **c** $y = 3 - x + 2\ln x$

  d $y = 3\ln x - 2x^{\frac{1}{2}}$ **e** $y = 4(2e^x - x)$ **f** $y = x^2 - 8x + 6\ln\frac{x}{3}$

7 Find an equation of the tangent to each curve at the point with the given x-coordinate.

  a $y = x^2 + 4\ln\frac{x}{2}$ $x = 2$ **b** $y = x^2 - 2x + 3e^x$ $x = 1$

  c $y = 2 - 4x - \ln 3x$ $x = \frac{1}{3}$ **d** $y = 4x^{\frac{1}{2}} - 4 - e^x$ $x = 4$

8 Find an equation of the normal to each curve at the point with the given x-coordinate.

  a $y = 5e^x - 7x$ $x = 0$ **b** $y = \ln 6x - x + 2$ $x = \frac{1}{2}$

  c $y = \frac{1}{2}e^x$ $x = 3$ **d** $y = x^{\frac{2}{3}} - 4\ln 2x$ $x = 8$

Exercise 16E	Exam Practice

1

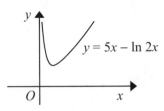

The diagram shows the curve with equation $y = 5x - \ln 2x$, $x > 0$.

  a Find in the form $ax + by + c = 0$ the equation of the tangent to
the curve at the point with x-coordinate $\frac{1}{2}$.   **(5 marks)**

  b Find in exact form the coordinates of the minimum point on the
curve.   **(3 marks)**

2
$$y = 2x + 4 \ln 5x, \ x > 0.$$

  a Find $\dfrac{d^2 y}{dx^2}$.   **(3 marks)**

  b Find the value of x for which

$$\frac{d^2 y}{dx^2} + \frac{dy}{dx} = 3.$$ **(4 marks)**

3

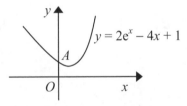

The diagram shows part of the curve $y = 2e^x - 4x + 1$.

  a Find in exact form the coordinates of the turning point of the curve.
    (4 marks)

The curve crosses the y-axis at the point A.

  b Find the area of the triangle enclosed by the normal to the curve
at A and the coordinate axes.   **(6 marks)**

4   The function f is given by

$$f : x \rightarrow 5 \ln 2x - x^{\frac{3}{2}}, \ x \in \mathbb{R}, \ x > 0.$$

  a Find in exact form a value for $f(e^2)$.   **(3 marks)**

  b Find, correct to 3 significant figures, the coordinates of the
stationary point on the curve $y = f(x)$.   **(6 marks)**

5

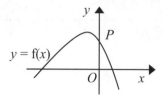

The diagram shows the curve $y = f(x)$ where

$$f(x) \equiv x - 2e^x + 6.$$

a Show that the range for f is given by

$$f(x) \le 5 - \ln 2.$$ **(5 marks)**

b Find an equation of the normal to the curve at the point P where it crosses the y-axis.   **(4 marks)**

c Show that the normal to the curve at the point P does not intersect the curve again.   **(3 marks)**

6 $$f(x) \equiv 3x^2 - 19x + 3 \ln 6x, \ x \in \mathbb{R}, \ x > 0.$$

a Find $f'(x)$.   **(2 marks)**

b Solve the equation $f'(x) = 0$.   **(3 marks)**

c Find in exact form the coordinates of the stationary points on the curve $y = f(x)$.   **(4 marks)**

7

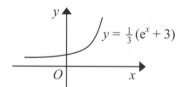

The diagram shows part of the curve $y = \frac{1}{3}(e^x + 3)$.

The curve passes through the point A with coordinates $(\ln 9, 4)$.

a Show that the tangent to the curve at A has the equation

$$y = 3x + 4 - 6 \ln 3.$$ **(4 marks)**

b Find an equation of the normal to the curve at A.   **(3 marks)**

The tangent and normal to the curve at A meet the y-axis at the points B and C respectively.

c Find the distance BC in the form $k \ln 3$.   **(4 marks)**

8   A curve has the equation $y = 4x^{\frac{1}{2}} + 2 \ln \frac{x}{2}$, $x > 0$, and passes through the point P $(2, 4\sqrt{2})$.

a Find the gradient of the curve at P.   **(4 marks)**

b Show that the tangent to the curve at P meets the x-axis at the point with coordinates $(4\sqrt{2} - 6, 0)$.   **(5 marks)**

Integration

Exercise 17S   Skills Practice

1 Integrate with respect to x.

a e^x **b** $5e^x$ **c** $\frac{3}{4}e^x$ **d** $\frac{1}{x}$ **e** $\frac{3}{x}$ **f** $\frac{1}{4x}$

2 Integrate with respect to y.

a $4y + e^y$ **b** $y^2 - y^{-1}$ **c** $3e^y + 2y^{-1}$

d $\frac{2}{3y} - 1 + 3y$ **e** $\frac{1}{5}e^y + \sqrt{y}$ **f** $(1 - \frac{1}{2\sqrt{y}})^2$

3 Find

a $\int 2x - 3e^x \, dx$ **b** $\int 3 - r^{-1} - r^{-2} \, dr$ **c** $\int (x+2)(x^{-1} - 3) \, dx$

d $\int \frac{y-2}{y} \, dy$ **e** $\int \frac{1}{2}(5e^t + t^2) \, dt$ **f** $\int \frac{x^2 - 4x + 2}{3x^2} \, dx$

4 Find f(x) in each case given f$'$(x) and the coordinates of a point on $y =$ f(x).

a $f'(x) \equiv 6x - \frac{2}{x}$ $(1, 3)$ **b** $f'(x) \equiv e^x - 5$ $(0, 2)$

c $f'(x) \equiv \frac{1}{x} + 6$ $(\frac{1}{3}, 2)$ **d** $f'(x) \equiv \frac{4x^2 + 1}{x}$ $(1, \ln 5)$

e $f'(x) \equiv 2x - 5 + e^x$ $(2, e^2 - 6)$ **f** $f'(x) \equiv \frac{4 - 3\sqrt{x}}{2x}$ $(4, 4\ln 2 + 1)$

5 Evaluate

a $\int_0^2 e^x - 1 \, dx$ **b** $\int_1^4 \frac{2x+1}{x} \, dx$ **c** $\int_0^{\ln 3} 2 + 5e^y \, dy$

d $\int_4^8 \frac{1}{4}x - 2x^{-1} \, dx$ **e** $\int_{-1}^1 t^2 + 2 - e^t \, dt$ **f** $\int_1^4 3\sqrt{x} + \frac{1}{2x} \, dx$

g $\int_{-3}^{-1} \frac{x^3 + 8}{4x} \, dx$ **h** $\int_1^{e^2} 2r^{-1} - 3 \, dr$ **i** $\int_{\frac{1}{2}}^1 (x - \frac{2}{x^2})^2 \, dx$

6

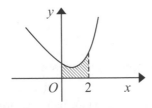

The shaded region on the diagram is enclosed by the curve $y = e^x - 2x$, the line $x = 2$ and the coordinate axes.

Find the area of the shaded region expressed in terms of e.

7

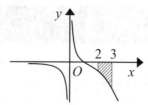

The shaded region on the diagram is enclosed by the curve $y = \frac{1}{x} - \frac{1}{3}e^x$, the ordinates $x = 2$ and $x = 3$, and the x-axis.

Show that the area of the shaded region is 3.83 correct to 3 significant figures.

8

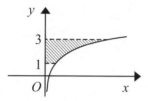

The shaded region on the diagram is enclosed by the curve $y = \ln x$, the lines $y = 1$ and $y = 3$, and the y-axis.

a   Write the equation of the curve in the form $x = f(y)$.

b   Show that the area of the shaded region is $e(e^2 - 1)$.

9   Find in each case the area of the region enclosed by the given curve and lines.

a $y = 2x + 3x^{-1}$ $x = 1$ $x = 3$ $y = 0$

b $y = 3e^x - x^2$ $x = 0$ $x = 1$ $y = 0$

c $y = \frac{1}{2}e^x + \frac{3}{x}$ $x = 1$ $x = 4$ $y = 0$

d $y = \dfrac{8 - x^3}{4x}$ $x = {}^-4$ $x = {}^-2$ $y = 0$

e $y = \ln 2x$ $x = 0$ $y = 0$ $y = 4$

f $y = \frac{2}{x}$ $x = 0$ $y = 1$ $y = 5$

10

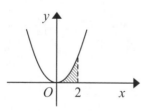

The shaded region on the diagram is enclosed by the curve $y = x^2$, the line $x = 2$ and the x-axis.

Show that the volume of the solid generated when the shaded region is rotated through 360° about the x-axis is $\frac{32}{5}\pi$.

11

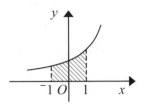

The shaded region on the diagram is enclosed by the curve $y = 3e^{\frac{x}{2}}$, the lines $x = {}^-1$ and $x = 1$, and the x-axis.

Find, in terms of π and e, the volume of the solid formed when the shaded region is rotated through 2π radians about the x-axis.

12   Find in each case the volume of the solid formed when the region enclosed by the given curve and lines is rotated through $360°$ about the x-axis.

a $y = 2x^{\frac{3}{2}}$ $\qquad\qquad$ $x = 3$ $\qquad$ $y = 0$

b $y = 1 - x^2$ $\qquad\qquad$ $y = 0$

c $y = 2x^{-1}$ $\qquad\qquad$ $x = {}^-6$ $\qquad$ $x = {}^-2$ $\qquad$ $y = 0$

d $y = 3x - x^2$ $\qquad\qquad$ $y = 0$

e $y = \frac{4}{x} - 1$ $\qquad\qquad$ $x = 2$ $\qquad$ $y = 0$

f $y = 1 + 2x^{-\frac{1}{2}}$ $\qquad$ $x = 1$ $\qquad$ $x = e^2$ $\qquad$ $y = 0$

13

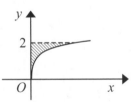

The shaded region on the diagram is enclosed by the curve $y = 2x^{\frac{1}{4}}$, the line $y = 2$ and the y-axis.

a   Write the equation of the curve in the form $x = f(y)$.

b   Show that when the shaded region is rotated through 2π radians about the y-axis the volume of the solid formed is $\frac{2}{9}\pi$.

14   Find in each case the volume of the solid formed when the area enclosed by the given curve and lines is rotated through 2π radians about the y-axis.

a $y = 2 \ln x$ $\qquad\qquad$ $x = 0$ $\qquad$ $y = 0$ $\qquad$ $y = 4$

b $y = x^{\frac{3}{2}}$ $\qquad\qquad$ $x = 0$ $\qquad$ $y = 1$ $\qquad$ $y = 8$

c $x = y^2 + 2y$ $\qquad\qquad$ $x = 0$

d $y = \dfrac{1}{2x - 3}$ $\qquad\quad$ $x = 0$ $\qquad$ $y = 3$ $\qquad$ $y = 9$

Exercise 17E   Exam Practice

1   **a** Expand $(x - 2)(3x - x^{-2})$ as a series in descending powers of x.   **(2 marks)**

   b Hence evaluate

$$\int_{\frac{1}{3}}^{3} (x - 2)(3x - x^{-2})\ dx,$$

giving your answer in terms of natural logarithms.   **(5 marks)**

2

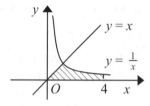

The shaded region on the diagram is enclosed by the curve
$y = \frac{1}{x}$, $x > 0$, the lines $y = x$ and $x = 4$, and the x-axis.

   a Show that the area of the shaded region is $\frac{1}{4}(4 \ln 2 + 1)$.   **(6 marks)**

   b Find, in terms of π, the volume of the solid formed when the
shaded region is rotated through $360°$ about the x-axis.   **(6 marks)**

3   **a** Find

$$\int x - 2 + 3e^{x}\ dx.$$ **(2 marks)**

Given that $f'(x) \equiv x - 2 + 3e^{x}$ and that the curve $y = f(x)$ passes
through the point $(0, {}^{-}4)$,

   b find $f(x)$.   **(2 marks)**

4

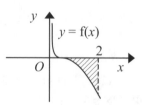

The diagram shows the curve with equation $y = f(x)$ where

$$f(x) \equiv \frac{(1 - 2x)^{3}}{x^{2}},\ \ x \in \mathbb{R},\ x > 0.$$

   a Express $f(x)$ as a series in ascending powers of x.   **(3 marks)**

The shaded region is bounded by the curve, the line $x = 2$ and
the x-axis.

   b Show that the area of the shaded region is $\frac{1}{2}(24 \ln 2 - 9)$.   **(7 marks)**

5   **a** Find

$$\int \frac{2\sqrt{x}+1}{3x} \; dx.$$ **(4 marks)**

b Hence show that

$$\int_1^{e^2} \frac{2\sqrt{x}+1}{3x} \; dx = \tfrac{2}{3}(2e-1).$$ **(4 marks)**

6

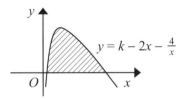

The diagram shows the curve with equation $y = k - 2x - \frac{4}{x}$, $x > 0$.

Given that the point with coordinates $(\frac{3}{2}, \frac{10}{3})$ lies on the curve,

a find the value of k,   **(2 marks)**

b find the coordinates of the points where the curve crosses
the x-axis.   **(4 marks)**

The shaded region is bounded by the curve and the x-axis.

c Show that the area of the shaded region is $\frac{1}{4}(63 - 48 \ln 2)$.   **(5 marks)**

7   The region bounded by the curve $y = x^2 + x$ and the x-axis is rotated
through $360°$ about the x-axis.

Show that the volume of the solid generated is $\frac{1}{30}\pi$.   **(8 marks)**

8

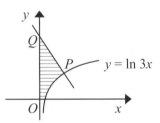

The diagram shows the curve $y = \ln 3x$ and the normal to the curve
at the point $P(2, \ln 6)$. The normal meets the y-axis at the point Q.

a Show that Q has coordinates $(0, 4 + \ln 6)$.   **(5 marks)**

b Express the equation of the curve in the form $x = f(y)$.   **(2 marks)**

c Show that the area of the shaded region enclosed by the curve,
the line PQ and the positive coordinate axes is $\frac{17}{3}$.   **(6 marks)**

Calculus Review

1   a Find

$$\int \frac{(x-2)^2}{x^2}\, dx.$$

(4 marks)

b Hence, evaluate

$$\int_2^{10} \frac{(x-2)^2}{x^2}\, dx,$$

giving your answer in the form $a + b \ln 5$.

(4 marks)

2

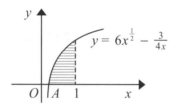

The diagram shows the curve $y = 6x^{\frac{1}{2}} - \frac{3}{4x}$ which crosses the x-axis at the point A with coordinates $(a, 0)$.

a Find the value of a.

(4 marks)

The shaded region is enclosed by the curve, the line $x = 1$ and the x-axis.

b Show that the area of the shaded region is $\frac{1}{2}(7 - 3 \ln 2)$.

(5 marks)

3

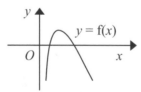

The diagram shows the curve with equation $y = f(x)$ where

$$f : x \rightarrow 2 \ln 6x - 9x^2, \ x \in \mathbb{R}, \ x > 0.$$

a Show that the maximum value of f is $(2 \ln 2 - 1)$.

(5 marks)

The point P lies on the curve and has coordinates $(\frac{1}{6}, k)$.

b Find the value of k.

(1 mark)

c Show that the tangent to the curve at P has the equation

$$36x - 4y - 7 = 0.$$

(4 marks)

4 Evaluate

$$\int_0^{\ln 3} 3 - 2e^x \ dx,$$

giving your answer in the form $a + b \ln 3$. **(4 marks)**

5

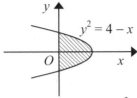

The diagram shows the curve $y^2 = 4 - x$.

a Find the coordinates of the three points where the curve crosses
the coordinate axes. **(3 marks)**

The shaded region is enclosed by the curve and the y-axis.

b Show that the volume of the solid formed when the shaded region
is rotated $360°$ about the y-axis is $\frac{512}{15}\pi$. **(6 marks)**

c Find the volume of the solid formed when the shaded region is
rotated $180°$ about the x-axis. **(5 marks)**

6 Given that

$$y = kx^2 - 5 + 3 \ln x,$$

and that for all positive values of x

$$x\frac{d^2y}{dx^2} + \frac{dy}{dx} - 6x = 0,$$

find the value of k. **(6 marks)**

7

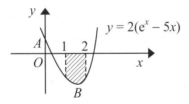

The diagram shows the curve $y = 2(e^x - 5x)$. The curve crosses
the y-axis at the point A and has a turning point at B.

a Find an equation of the tangent to the curve at A. **(5 marks)**

b Find in exact from the coordinates of the point B. **(3 marks)**

The shaded region is bounded by the curve, the ordinates $x = 1$ and
$x = 2$, and the x-axis.

c Show that the area of the shaded region is $(2e^2 - 2e - 15)$. **(4 marks)**

8

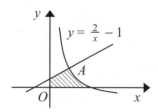

The diagram shows the curve $y = \frac{2}{x} - 1$, $x > 0$, and the normal to the curve at the point A (1, 1).

a   Find an equation of the normal to the curve at the point A.   **(4 marks)**

b   Find the area of the shaded region enclosed by the curve, the normal to the curve at A and the positive coordinate axes.   **(7 marks)**

9   Given that the curve $y = x^3 - 3e^x$ has a stationary point where $x = \alpha$,

a   show that $e^\alpha = \alpha^2$.   **(3 marks)**

Given also that $\alpha < 0$,

b   show that the stationary point is a maximum.   **(5 marks)**

10

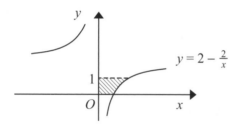

The diagram shows part of the curve $y = 2 - \frac{2}{x}$, $x \neq 0$.

The shaded region enclosed by the curve, the positive coordinate axes and the line $y = 1$ is rotated through 2π radians about the x-axis.

Show that the volume of the solid formed is $4\pi(2 \ln 2 - 1)$.   **(9 marks)**

11

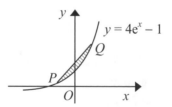

The diagram shows the curve $y = 4e^x - 1$. The points P and Q lie on the curve and have x-coordinates of $^-1$ and 1 respectively.

a   Find the length of the chord PQ correct to 3 significant figures.   **(4 marks)**

b   Show that the area of the shaded region bounded by the curve and the straight line PQ is $8e^{-1}$.   **(7 marks)**

Roots of Equations and Iteration

| Exercise 19S | Skills Practice |

1 $f(x) \equiv e^{x+1} - 6, \ x \in \mathbb{R}.$

   a Evaluate f(0.5) and f(1).

   b With the aid of a sketch, explain why your answers to part **a** show that there is
a root of the equation f(x) = 0 in the interval (0.5, 1).

$$g(x) \equiv \frac{1}{4x - 3}, \ x \in \mathbb{R}, \ x \neq 0.75$$

   c Evaluate g(0.5) and g(1).

   d By sketching the curve $y = g(x)$, explain why there is not a root of the equation
g(x) = 0 in the interval (0.5, 1).

2   Show in each case that there is a root of the equation f(x) = 0 in the given interval.

   a $f(x) \equiv x^3 + 2x - 5$ (1, 1.5)   **b** $f(x) \equiv x^2 - 6\sin x$ (2, 2.5)

   c $f(x) \equiv x^4 + 3x + 1$ ($^-$0.5, 0)   **d** $f(x) \equiv 4\ln x - x$ (8.6, 8.7)

   e $f(x) \equiv x^{\frac{3}{2}} - 7\cos 2x$ (3.3, 3.4)   **f** $f(x) \equiv e^{2x} - 3x - 5$ ($^-$1.7, $^-$1.6)

3   Find in each case the positive integer N such that there is a root of the equation
f(x) = 0 in the interval (N, N + 1)

   a $f(x) \equiv 2 + x^2 - x^3$ **b** $f(x) \equiv 2 + 8\sqrt{x} - x^2$ **c** $f(x) \equiv e^x + x - 9$

   d $f(x) \equiv \sin x - \ln \frac{x}{2}$ **e** $f(x) \equiv x^4 - 7x^3 - 10$ **f** $f(x) \equiv \frac{8}{x} - \ln x$

4   Show in each case that there is a root of the equation in the given interval.

   a $3\sin x = 2x$ (1, 1.5)   **b** $x^{\frac{4}{3}} = 2x^{\frac{1}{2}} + 1$ (3.1, 3.2)

   c $\frac{2}{x} = 1 - x^2$ ($^-$1.6, $^-$1.5)   **d** $e^{3x} = 2 - \ln x$ (0.36, 0.37)

   e $x = \cot 2x$ ($^-$0.6, $^-$0.5)   **f** $e^{-x} = \sin 3x$ (12.5, 12.6)

5   In each case there is a root of the equation f(x) = 0 in the given interval.
Find the integer, a, such that this root lies in the interval $(\frac{a}{10}, \frac{a+1}{10})$.

   a $f(x) \equiv 2x^3 + x - 2$ (0, 1)   **b** $f(x) \equiv x^2 - 4\sqrt{x} + 1$ (2, 3)

   c $f(x) \equiv 2\tan x - x + 1$ ($^-$1, 0)   **d** $f(x) \equiv \cos x - \ln x$ (0, 4)

   e $f(x) \equiv e^x - x^2 + 6$ ($^-$5, 0)   **f** $f(x) \equiv \frac{1}{x} - \sin \frac{x}{2}$ (10, 15)

6   **a** Show by calculation that the equation $e^{x-1} = 2x + 3$ has one positive and one
negative root.

   b Find each root correct to the nearest integer.

7   The equation $x^4 + 4x - 2 = 0$ has a root in the interval $(0, 1)$.

Use the iteration $x_{n+1} = \frac{1}{4}(2 - x_n^4)$ with $x_0 = 0.5$ to find the values of x_1, x_2, x_3 and x_4. Hence write down the value of the root correct to 3 sf.

8   The equation $x^3 - 6x + 2 = 0$ has a root in the interval $(2, 3)$.

Describe what happens when you use each of the following iterations with $x_0 = 2$ to attempt to find this root.

a $x_{n+1} = \dfrac{2}{6 - x_n^2}$

b $x_{n+1} = \sqrt{6 - \dfrac{2}{x_n}}$

c $x_{n+1} = \frac{1}{2} x_n^2 (6 - x_n^2)$

9   The equation $x^3 - 4x - 1 = 0$ has a root in the interval $(2, 3)$.

a   Use the iteration $x_{n+1} = \sqrt[3]{4x_n + 1}$ with $x_0 = 2$ to find this root correct to 3sf.

b   By calculating the value of $(x^3 - 4x - 1)$ for suitable values of x, justify the accuracy of your answer to part **a**.

10   For each equation show that it can be rearranged into the given iterative form. Use this and the given value of x_0 to find one root of the equation correct to 2 dp.

a $x^4 - 5x + 2 = 0$ $x_{n+1} = \frac{1}{5}(x_n^4 + 2)$ $x_0 = 0$

b $e^{2x} - 2x^3 = 6$ $x_{n+1} = \frac{1}{2} \ln(2x_n^3 + 6)$ $x_0 = 1$

c $\dfrac{2}{x^3} - 5 \sin x = 0$ $x_{n+1} = \sqrt[3]{\dfrac{2}{5 \sin x_n}}$ $x_0 = {}^-1$

d $x^{\frac{3}{2}} + x^{\frac{1}{2}} = 3x$ $x_{n+1} = \left(\dfrac{3x_n}{x_n + 1}\right)^2$ $x_0 = 5$

11   Justify the accuracy of your answers to question **10**.

12   The equation $x^4 = 2x^3 + 6$ has two roots.

a   Use the iteration $x_{n+1} = \sqrt{2x_n + \dfrac{6}{x_n^2}}$ with $x_0 = 2$ to find one root correct to 3 sf.

b   Use an iteration of the form $x_{n+1} = \sqrt[3]{\dfrac{a}{x_n + b}}$ with $x_0 = {}^-1$ to find the other root correct to 3 sf.

13   For each equation use an iteration of the given form and the given value of x_0 to find one root of the equation correct to 3 sf.

a $2x \operatorname{cosec} x - 3 = 0$ $x_{n+1} = a \sin x_n$ $x_0 = 1$

b $x^3 - 8x + 1 = 0$ $x_{n+1} = \sqrt[3]{ax_n + b}$ $x_0 = 3$

c $2 \ln(5x - 1) = x$ $x_{n+1} = \frac{1}{5}(e^{ax_n} + b)$ $x_0 = 0.5$

d $x^3 - 3 = 8x - 5x^2$ $x_{n+1} = \dfrac{a + bx_n^2}{x_n^2 + c}$ $x_0 = {}^-0.3$

Exercise 19E Exam Practice

1 The equation $2x^{-1} + 3x^{\frac{1}{2}} - 8 = 0$ has two roots.

    a Show that one root lies in the interval $(0.2, 0.4)$. **(2 marks)**

    b Using the iterative formula

$$x_{n+1} = \frac{2}{8 - 3\sqrt{x_n}},$$

    with $x_0 = 0.3$, find this root correct to 3 decimal places and justify
the accuracy of your answer. **(5 marks)**

    c Find the positive integer, N, such that the other root lies in the
interval $(N, N+1)$. **(3 marks)**

2 $$f : x \to x^2 - 3x - \cos x, \quad x \in \mathbb{R}.$$

    a By sketching the curves $y = x^2 - 3x$ and $y = \cos x$ on the same
diagram, show that the equation $f(x) = 0$ has two roots. **(4 marks)**

    b The iterative formula $x_{n+1} = \frac{\cos x_n}{x_n - 3}$ is to be used with $x_0 = 0$ to
find one of these roots.

      i Find the values of x_1, x_2, x_3, x_4 and x_5.

      ii Without further calculation explain how your answers show
that this root is $^-0.291$ correct to 3 significant figures. **(5 marks)**

    c Using an iterative formula of the form $x_{n+1} = a + \frac{\cos x_n}{x_n}$, with a
suitable value of x_0 which should be stated, find the other root
correct to 3 significant figures. **(5 marks)**

3

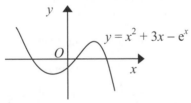

$$y = x^2 + 3x - e^x$$

The diagram shows part of the curve $y = x^2 + 3x - e^x$ which crosses
the x-axis at three points.

    a Show that the x-coordinate, α, of one of these points lies in the
interval $0 < \alpha < 1$ and find the integer n such that $\frac{n}{10} < \alpha < \frac{n+1}{10}$. **(5 marks)**

The curve has two stationary points.

    b Show that the x-coordinate, β, of one of these points lies in the
interval $1 < \beta < 2$. **(4 marks)**

    c Use an iterative formula of the form $x_{n+1} = \ln(ax_n + b)$, with
$x_0 = 2$ to find β correct to 3 significant figures. **(4 marks)**

The Trapezium Rule

Exercise 20S   Skills Practice

1   The table below gives the value of f(x) correct to 2 dp for certain values of x.

x	2	2.5	3	3.5	4	4.5	5
f(x)	9.78	7.12	5.90	6.23	6.88	7.57	8.35

Use the trapezium rule with 6 intervals of equal width to estimate the area
enclosed by the curve $y = f(x)$, the ordinates $x = 2$ and $x = 5$, and the x-axis.

2   **a** Sketch the curve $y = 8x - x^2$ and estimate the area enclosed by the curve and
the x-axis using the trapezium rule with 4 intervals of equal width.

   b Find this area exactly using integration and hence calculate the percentage
error in your answer to part **a**.

3

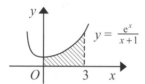

The shaded region on the diagram is enclosed by the curve $y = \frac{e^x}{x+1}$, the line $x = 3$
and the coordinate axes. Show that using the trapezium rule with 4 equally spaced
ordinates this area can be estimated as $\frac{1}{24}(12 + 12e + 8e^2 + 3e^3)$.

4   In each case estimate the area of the region enclosed by the given curve and lines
using the trapezium rule with the specified number of intervals of equal width.

   a $y = \sqrt{3x+1}$ $x = 0$ $x = 1$ $y = 0$ 3 intervals

   b $y = \frac{2}{x-3}$ $x = 4$ $x = 6$ $y = 0$ 4 intervals

   c $y = x^2 - \ln x$ $x = 1$ $x = 4$ $y = 0$ 3 intervals

   d $y = x \sin x$ $x = 0$ $x = \pi$ $y = 0$ 4 intervals

5   Use the trapezium rule with the stated number of intervals of equal width to
estimate the value of each integral correct to 3 sf.

   a $\int_0^3 \sqrt{x^2+6}\ dx$ 3 intervals   **b** $\int_1^3 \ln(4x-1)\ dx$ 4 intervals

   c $\int_2^{10} \frac{x+4}{x-1}\ dx$ 8 intervals   **d** $\int_{\frac{\pi}{3}}^{\frac{5\pi}{3}} \csc\frac{x}{2}\ dx$ 4 intervals

   e $\int_0^1 (e^x - 1)^2\ dx$ 5 intervals   **f** $\int_{-6}^{-2} \frac{x^2-1}{2-x}\ dx$ 4 intervals

Exercise 20E	Exam Practice

1 Using the trapezium rule with 6 equally spaced ordinates, calculate an approximate value for the integral

$$\int_3^8 \sqrt{2x-3}\ dx,$$

giving your answer correct to 2 decimal places. **(5 marks)**

2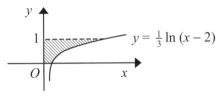

The diagram shows the curve $y = \frac{1}{3}\ln(x-2)$, $x > 2$.

a Write the equation of the curve in the form $x = f(y)$. **(2 marks)**

The shaded region on the diagram is enclosed by the curve, the line $y = 1$ and the coordinate axes. The area of the shaded region is to be estimated using the trapezium rule with 3 intervals of equal width.

b Show that this gives a value of $\frac{1}{6}(13 + 2e + 2e^2 + e^3)$. **(6 marks)**

3 Use the trapezium rule with 4 intervals of equal width to estimate the value of

$$\int_2^4 \frac{x+3}{2x-1}\ dx,$$

giving your answer correct to 3 significant figures. **(6 marks)**

4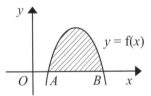

The diagram shows the curve with equation $y = f(x)$ where

$$f(x) \equiv 4\sin x - \operatorname{cosec} x, \quad x \in \mathbb{R},\ 0 < x < \pi.$$

The curve cuts the x-axis at the points A and B.

a Find the x-coordinates of the points A and B. **(5 marks)**

The shaded region is bounded by the curve and the x-axis.

b Show that using the trapezium rule with 4 intervals of equal width gives an estimate of $\frac{\pi}{18}(9 + 8\sqrt{3})$ for the area of the shaded region. **(7 marks)**

Numerical Methods Review

Exercise 21E   Exam Practice

1

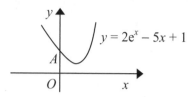

The diagram shows the curve $y = 2e^x - 5x + 1$ which crosses the y-axis at the point A.

a   Find an equation of the normal to the curve at the point A.   **(6 marks)**

The normal to the curve at A meets the curve again at the point B.

b   Show that the x-coordinate of B is given by a solution of the equation $3e^x - 8x - 3 = 0$.   **(3 marks)**

c   Show that the x-coordinate of B lies in the interval $(1, 2)$ and find the integer N such that it lies in the interval $\left(\frac{N}{10}, \frac{N+1}{10}\right)$.   **(5 marks)**

2   **a**   Use the trapezium rule with 5 equally spaced ordinates to estimate the value of the integral

$$\int_0^\pi 1 + \sin^2 x \; dx,$$

giving your answer in terms of π.   **(6 marks)**

b   Hence, giving a reason for your answer, write down an approximate value for the integral

$$\int_{-\pi}^\pi 1 + \sin^2 x \; dx.$$ **(2 marks)**

3

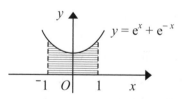

The shaded region on the diagram is enclosed by the curve $y = e^x + e^{-x}$, the lines $x = {}^-1$ and $x = 1$, and the x-axis.

a   Show that when the shaded region is rotated through 2π radians about the x-axis, the volume of the solid generated is given by

$$\pi \int_{-1}^1 e^{2x} + 2 + e^{-2x} \; dx.$$ **(3 marks)**

b   Using the trapezium rule with 5 equally spaced ordinates, estimate this volume giving your answer correct to 1 decimal place.   **(6 marks)**

4 $f : x \to x^4 - x^2 + 2x - 3, \ x \in \mathbb{R}.$

a By sketching the curves $y = x^4 - 3$ and $y = x^2 - 2x$ on the same
diagram, show that the equation $f(x) = 0$ has two roots.   **(4 marks)**

b Show that one root lies in the interval $(1.1, 1.3)$ and use an
iteration of the form

$$x_{n+1} = \sqrt[3]{x + a + bx^{-1}},$$

with $x_0 = 1.2$ to find this root correct to 4 significant figures.   **(7 marks)**

5   **a** Sketch the curve $y = f(x)$ where

$$f(x) \equiv \frac{1}{2x - 3}, \ x \in \mathbb{R}, \ x > 2,$$

and shade the region enclosed by the curve, the lines $x = 3$ and
$x = 7$, and the x-axis.   **(4 marks)**

b Use the trapezium rule with 5 equally spaced ordinates to estimate
the area of the shaded region correct to 3 decimal places.   **(5 marks)**

c State, with a reason, whether the actual area of the shaded region
is more or less than your answer to part **b**.   **(2 marks)**

6

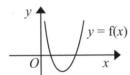

The diagram shows the curve $y = f(x)$ where

$$f(x) \equiv x^3 + x - 6 \ln 2x, \ x \in \mathbb{R}, \ x > 0.$$

The curve is stationary when $x = \alpha.$

a Show that $1 < \alpha < 2.$ **(5 marks)**

b Use an iteration of the form

$$x_{n+1} = \sqrt[3]{a + bx_n},$$

with $x_0 = 1$ to find α correct to 4 significant figures and justify
the accuracy of your answer.   **(6 marks)**

c Hence find the minimum value of f correct to 3 significant figures. **(2 marks)**

7   The table below gives the value of $f(x)$ for certain values of x.

x	$^-2$	$^-1$	0	1	2	3	4
$f(x)$	0.35	0.92	1.73	3.10	4.96	4.85	4.22

Use the trapezium rule with 6 intervals of equal width to find an
approximate value for the integral

$$\int_0^6 3f(x - 2) \ dx,$$

giving your answer correct to 1 decimal place.   **(7 marks)**

Proof

Exercise 22S   Skills Practice

1   Find a counter-example to disprove each statement.

    a   All prime numbers are odd.

    b   If x and y are integers and $(x + y)$ is even, then x and y are both even.

    c   If a, b and c are integers and bc is divisible by a, then b is divisible by a.

    d $(2^n + 3)$ is prime for all positive integers n.

    e   If x and y are irrational, then xy is irrational.

2   Use direct proof to show that each statement is true.

    a   If n is an even integer, then n^2 is divisible by 4.

    b   If a and b are rational, then $(a + b)$ is rational.

    c   If $f(x) \equiv x^2 - 6x + 10$, then $\left| f(x) \right| = f(x)$ for all real values of x.

    d   Every odd integer can be written as the difference of two perfect squares.

    e $\tan^2 x - \sin^2 x \equiv \sin^2 x \tan^2 x, \ x \neq \dfrac{(2n+1)\pi}{2}, \ n \in \mathbb{Z}$.

3   Use proof by contradiction to show that each statement is true.

    a   For integers a, b and c, if bc is not divisible by a, then b is not divisible by a.

    b $\sqrt{2}$ is irrational.

    c   There are no positive integer solutions to the equation $x^2 - y^2 = 1$.

    d   If x is irrational, then $\sqrt{x}$ is irrational.

    e   If p and q are integers and q is odd, then the equation $x^2 + 2px + 2q = 0$ has no rational solutions.

4   For each statement, either prove that it is true or find a counter-example to prove that it is false.

    a   If a and b are real numbers and $a^2 > b^2$ then $a > b$.

    b   If a, b and c are integers and b and c are divisible by a, then $(b + c)$ is divisible by a.

    c $\sqrt{n}$ is irrational for all positive integers n.

    d $(n^3 + n + 1)$ is prime for all positive integers n.

    e   Any integer divisible by 4 can be written as the difference of two perfect squares.

    f   There is no smallest positive rational number.

    g $\sin 2A - \cos A \equiv \sin A \cos 2A$ for all A.

Exercise 22E	**Exam Practice**

1 Show that each of the following statements is false by finding a counter-example.

   a If $x^2 = 3x$, then $x = 3$. **(1 mark)**

   b If a and b are irrational and $a \neq b$, then $(a - b)$ is irrational. **(2 marks)**

   c $(4^n + 3)$ is prime for all positive integers n. **(3 marks)**

2 Use proof by contradiction to show that if
$$x^3 - 3 = 0,$$
then x is irrational. **(7 marks)**

3   **a** Find a counter-example to disprove the following statement:

       "$1 + \sin x > 2 \sin x$, for all real values of x." **(2 marks)**

   b Prove that, for $\sin 2A \neq \sin 2B$,

     $\dfrac{\sin 2A + \sin 2B}{\sin 2A - \sin 2B} \equiv \tan(A + B) \cot(A - B)$. **(5 marks)**

4 For each statement, either prove that it is true or find a counter-example to prove that it is false.

   a If ab is rational and $a \neq b$, then a and b are both rational. **(2 marks)**

   b If a and b are consecutive odd integers, then $(a + b)$ is divisible by 4. **(4 marks)**

   c If a is irrational and b is an integer, then $\log_b a$ is irrational. **(3 marks)**

5   **a** By completing the square, or otherwise, prove the statement

     "if $x^2 + xy + y^2 = 0$, then $x = y = 0$." **(5 marks)**

   b Using proof by contradiction, prove the statement

     "if a is rational and b is irrational, then $(a + b)$ is irrational." **(5 marks)**

6 Find a counter-example to disprove each statement.

   a If $(a + b)^2 = c^2$, then $(a + b) = c$. **(3 marks)**

   b $(n^2 + 3n + 13)$ is prime for all positive integers n. **(4 marks)**

7 Prove each of the following identities:

   a $\tan \theta + \cot \theta \equiv \sec \theta \, \mathrm{cosec}\, \theta$, $\theta \neq \dfrac{n\pi}{2}$, $n \in \mathbb{Z}$. **(5 marks)**

   b $\dfrac{\sin x}{1 - \cos x} \equiv \dfrac{\cos x + 1}{\sin x}$, $x \neq n\pi$, $n \in \mathbb{Z}$. **(5 marks)**

8   **a** Find a counter-example to disprove the statement:

"If $x > y$, then $xz > yz$ for all real values of x, y and z." **(2 marks)**

   b Use proof by contradiction to show that if x and y are integers and $(3x^2 - y^2)$ is divisible by 4, then x and y cannot both be odd. **(6 marks)**

9   For each statement, either prove that it is true or find a counter-example to prove that it is false.

   a If $x > 0$, then $\sqrt{x} < x$ for all real values of x. **(2 marks)**

   b If $(x + y)$ is rational, then both x and y are rational. **(3 marks)**

   c $\sec\left(\frac{\pi}{2} - x\right) \equiv \operatorname{cosec} x$, for $x \neq n\pi$, $n \in \mathbb{Z}$. **(4 marks)**

10 Use proof by contradiction to show that there are no positive integer solutions to the equation

$$x^2 - y^2 = 6.$$ **(7 marks)**

11 Prove each of the following statements.

   a If b is divisible by a and c is divisible by b, then c is divisible by a, where a, b and c are integers. **(3 marks)**

   b For $\cos x \neq 0$,

$$(\tan x + 1)^2 \equiv \frac{1 + \sin 2x}{\cos^2 x}.$$ **(5 marks)**

12 **a** Prove that if p and q are odd integers, then pq is an odd integer. **(3 marks)**

   b Hence deduce that if p is an odd integer, then p^n is an odd integer for all positive integral values of n. **(3 marks)**

   c Hence, or otherwise, use proof by contradiction to show that $\log_2 5$ is irrational. **(5 marks)**

13 **a** Prove the identity

$$\tan x \equiv \frac{1 - \cos 2x}{\sin 2x}, \quad x \neq \frac{n\pi}{2}, \ n \in \mathbb{Z}.$$ **(5 marks)**

   b Prove that if $(a^2 - 1)$ is divisible by 3 then a is not divisible by 3. **(5 marks)**

14 **a** Given that m and n are integers, prove that the expression

$$m^3 + mn^2 + n^3$$

   is even only if both m and n are even. **(6 marks)**

   b Hence, use proof by contradiction to show that there are no rational solutions to the equation

$$x^3 + x + 1 = 0.$$ **(5 marks)**

Course Review

Exercise 23E	Exam Practice

1 Find, correct to 3 significant figures, the values of x and y such that

a $4^{x+2} = 35$, **(3 marks)**

b $2 \ln (4 - 3y) - 7 = 0$. **(4 marks)**

2 a Use the identity

$$\cos(A + B) \equiv \cos A \cos B - \sin A \sin B,$$

to prove the identity

$$\cos^2 A \equiv \tfrac{1}{2}(1 + \cos 2A).$$ **(4 marks)**

b Hence, or otherwise, express $\cos^4 x$ in the form

$$p + q \cos 2x + r \cos 4x,$$

where p, q and r are rational numbers. **(5 marks)**

3

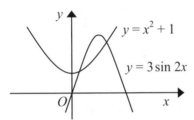

The diagram shows part of the curves $y = x^2 + 1$ and $y = 3 \sin 2x$ which intersect at two points.

a Show that the x-coordinate of one of these points of intersection lies in the interval $(0.1, 0.2)$. **(3 marks)**

b Use the iterative formula

$$x_{n+1} = \sqrt{2x_n + 3 \sin 2x_n} - 1,$$

with $x_0 = 1$ to find the x-coordinate of the other point of intersection correct to 3 significant figures. **(5 marks)**

4 $$f(x) \equiv ax - \frac{a}{x}, \quad x \in \mathbb{R}, \ x > 0.$$

Given that

$$\int_1^2 f(x) \ dx = 3 - 2 \ln 2,$$

find the value of the constant a. **(4 marks)**

5   Express

$$\frac{2y-1}{6y-12} - \frac{y}{y+3} - \frac{3y-1}{2y^2+2y-12}$$

as a single fraction in its simplest form.   **(7 marks)**

6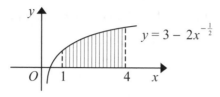

The diagram shows the curve with equation $y = 3 - 2x^{-\frac{1}{2}}$, $x > 0$.

a   Express y^2 in the form

$$A + Bx^{-\frac{1}{2}} + Cx^{-1}.$$ **(2 marks)**

The shaded region enclosed by the curve, the lines $x = 1$ and $x = 4$, and the x-axis is rotated through 2π radians about the x-axis.

b   Show that the volume of the solid formed is $\pi(3 + 8\ln 2)$.   **(6 marks)**

7   The functions f and g are defined by

$$f : x \rightarrow \frac{x+1}{2x-3}, \quad x \in \mathbb{R}, \ x \neq p.$$

$$g : x \rightarrow \frac{x-1}{x-2}, \quad x \in \mathbb{R}, \ x \neq q.$$

a   Write down the values of p and q.   **(1 mark)**

b   Define the inverse function, $f^{-1}(x)$, stating its domain clearly.   **(5 marks)**

c   Prove that there are no real values of x for which $f(x) = g(x)$.   **(5 marks)**

d   Show that

$$gg(x) \equiv \frac{1}{3-x},$$

and state its domain.   **(5 marks)**

8    $$f(x) \equiv (1 - x)^{12} - (1 - 2x)^6.$$

a   Show that the series expansion of $f(x)$ up to and including the term in x^3 is given by

$$f(x) = 6x^2 - 60x^3.$$ **(7 marks)**

b   Using this result and a suitable value of x which should be stated, estimate the value of $[(0.99)^{12} - (0.98)^6]$ correct to 2 significant figures.   **(3 marks)**

c   Explain why the expansion obtained in part **a** would be less accurate if used to estimate the value of $[(0.95)^{12} - (0.9)^6]$.   **(2 marks)**

9   The temperature, $\theta\,°C$, of a cup of hot cocoa t minutes after it is made is given by

$$\theta = 64(2^{-\frac{1}{10}t}) + 22.$$

   a   Find the initial temperature of the hot cocoa. **(2 marks)**

   b   Find the temperature of the cocoa after 20 minutes. **(2 marks)**

   c   Find how long it takes for the cocoa to cool to a temperature of 30°C. **(4 marks)**

   d   State the temperature of the cocoa after it has been left standing for a long time. **(1 mark)**

10 A sequence of numbers $t_1, t_2, t_3, \ldots$ is defined by the recurrence relation

$$t_{n+1} = 3t_n - 4.$$

   a   Describe the behaviour of the sequence when

     i $t_1 = 2$,

     ii $t_1 = 3$. **(4 marks)**

The terms of another sequence of numbers $u_1, u_2, u_3, \ldots$ are linked to the terms of the first sequence as follows:

$$u_n = t_n - 2.$$

   b   Show that

$$u_{n+1} = 3u_n. \qquad \textbf{(4 marks)}$$

   c   Find an expression for u_n in terms of n and u_1. **(3 marks)**

   d   Hence, or otherwise, show that

$$t_n = 3^{n-1}(t_1 - 2) + 2. \qquad \textbf{(3 marks)}$$

11 Find any values of x for which

$$3^{2x+1} - 26(3^x) - 9 = 0. \qquad \textbf{(5 marks)}$$

12 a   Find the exact value of

$$\int_2^4 \frac{1}{x}\,dx. \qquad \textbf{(3 marks)}$$

A student programs a calculator to estimate the value of integrals using the trapezium rule with 5 equally spaced ordinates.

   b   Find, correct to 4 decimal places, the value that should be obtained for the integral in part **a** using this program. **(5 marks)**

   c   Show that the percentage error involved in using the program in this case is 0.56%, correct to 2 significant figures. **(2 marks)**

13 The current, I Amps, in an electrical circuit t seconds after it is switched on is given by

$$I = 6\cos(180t)^\circ + 9\sin(180t)^\circ.$$

a Express I in the form $R\sin(180t + \alpha)^\circ$ where $R > 0$ and $0 < \alpha < 90$.   **(5 marks)**

By mistake, an 8 Amp fuse is fitted in the circuit. The fuse blows and breaks the circuit as soon as the current reaches 8 Amps.

b Find, correct to 2 significant figures, the value of t when the circuit is broken.   **(4 marks)**

14 **a** Show that the equation

$$\log_2(y + 3) - 1 = 2\log_2 x$$

can be rewritten as

$$y = 2x^2 - 3.$$ **(4 marks)**

b Hence, or otherwise, find all pairs (x, y) of solutions to the simultaneous equations

$$\log_2(y + 3) - 1 = 2\log_2 x,$$
$$\log_2(y - 5x + 6) = 0.$$ **(5 marks)**

15

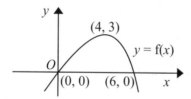

The diagram shows the curve $y = f(x)$ which meets the coordinate axes at the points $(0, 0)$ and $(6, 0)$ and is stationary at the point $(4, 3)$.

Showing the coordinates of any points where each curve meets the coordinate axes, and of any stationary points, sketch on separate diagrams graphs of

a $y = f(2x)$,   **(2 marks)**

b $y = f(|x|)$,   **(3 marks)**

c $y = \frac{1}{2} f(x + 6)$.   **(4 marks)**

16 **a** Completely factorise the expression

$$x^3 - x.$$ **(1 mark)**

b Prove that if n is a positive integer greater than 1, then $(n^3 - n)$ is a multiple of 6.   **(4 marks)**

17

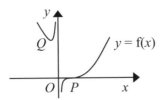

The diagram shows the curve with equation $y = f(x)$ where

$$f(x) \equiv \frac{(x-2)^3}{x}, \quad x \in \mathbb{R}, \ x \neq 0.$$

a Express $(x-2)^3$ as series in descending powers of x. **(2 marks)**

b Hence, express $f'(x)$ in the form $\dfrac{Ax^3 + Bx^2 + C}{x^2}$. **(3 marks)**

The point $P\,(2, 0)$ lies on the curve.

c Show that the curve is stationary at P. **(2 marks)**

d Hence find the coordinates of the other stationary point on the curve, Q. **(6 marks)**

18 **a** Given that

$$\tan \theta + \sec \theta = 2\cos \theta,$$

show that

$$2\sin^2 \theta + \sin \theta - 1 = 0.$$ **(4 marks)**

b Hence find the values of x in the interval $0 \leq x \leq 2\pi$ for which

$$\tan 2x + \sec 2x = 2\cos 2x,$$

giving your answers in terms of π. **(6 marks)**

19 The equation of a curve is $y = ax^n$ where a and n are positive constants.

The curve passes through the point $(2, 3)$ and the point $(8, 9)$.

a Find the value of n correct to 3 significant figures. **(4 marks)**

b Find the exact value of a. **(5 marks)**

20 A sequence is defined by the recurrence relation

$$u_{n+1} = \frac{1}{1-u_n}, \quad n \geq 1.$$

Given that $u_1 = k$,

a show that $u_3 = \dfrac{k-1}{k}$, **(4 marks)**

b find and simplify an expression for u_4 in terms of k. **(3 marks)**

Given also that $u_{50} = 2$,

c find k. **(4 marks)**

21   The function f is defined by

$$f : x \rightarrow 9x + \frac{4}{x}, \ x \in \mathbb{R}, \ x \neq 0.$$

   a   Prove that f is an odd function.   **(3 marks)**

   b   Show that

$$\int_1^e f(x) \ dx \ = \ \tfrac{1}{2}(9e^2 - 1).$$ **(4 marks)**

22   The coefficients of x^2 and x^3 in the expansion of $(1 + kx)^n$ are equal.
   Given that n is a positive integer,

   a   show that $n = \dfrac{2k+3}{k}$.   **(6 marks)**

   Given also that the coefficient of x in the expansion is 6,

   b   find the value of k,   **(2 marks)**

   c   find the coefficient of x^4.   **(3 marks)**

23 $$f(x) \equiv 6x^2 - 5x - 6.$$

   a   Find the set of values of x for which $f(x) \leq 0$.   **(3 marks)**

   b   Hence, sketch the curve $y = |f(x)|$ labelling the coordinates of
   any points where the curve meets the coordinate axes.   **(4 marks)**

24 $$f(x) \equiv \sin x + \sqrt{3} \cos x.$$

   A student is attempting to solve the equation $f(x) = 1$ for values of x
   in the interval $0 \leq x \leq 360°$ and writes the following:

$$\sin x + \sqrt{3} \cos x = 1$$
$$\sqrt{3} \cos x = 1 - \sin x$$
$$3 \cos^2 x = (1 - \sin x)^2$$
$$3(1 - \sin^2 x) = 1 - 2\sin x + \sin^2 x$$
$$4 \sin^2 x - 2 \sin x - 2 = 0$$
$$2(\sin x - 1)(2 \sin x + 1) = 0$$
$$\sin x = -\tfrac{1}{2} \text{ or } 1$$
$$x = 90°, 210°, 330°$$

   a   Show that one of the values found by the student is not a solution
   of the equation $f(x) = 1$.   **(3 marks)**

   b   Explain how the incorrect solution has been introduced.   **(2 marks)**

   Another student attempts to solve the equation $f(x) = 1$ by first
   writing $f(x)$ in the form $R \sin(x + \alpha)$ with $0 < \alpha < 90°$.

   c   Find the value of α that this student should use and the
   corresponding value of R.   **(5 marks)**

25 **a** Find the values of x for which

$$\frac{x-1}{x-2} - \frac{x-3}{x+2} = \frac{4}{3}.$$ **(5 marks)**

b Hence, or otherwise, solve the equations

i $\dfrac{t^{\frac{1}{2}}-1}{t^{\frac{1}{2}}-2} - \dfrac{t^{\frac{1}{2}}-3}{t^{\frac{1}{2}}+2} = \dfrac{4}{3},$

ii $\dfrac{\sin 2y - 1}{\sin 2y - 2} - \dfrac{\sin 2y - 3}{\sin 2y + 2} = \dfrac{4}{3},$ for $0 \le y \le 2\pi.$ **(6 marks)**

26 Find all solutions to the equation

$$x + 2a = \left|3a - 2x\right|,$$

where a is a positive constant. **(4 marks)**

27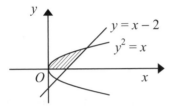

The diagram shows the line $y = x - 2$ and the curve $y^2 = x.$

a Find the coordinates of the points where the line and curve meet. **(4 marks)**

The shaded region is bounded by the line, the curve and the x-axis such that $y \ge 0$ for points in the region.

b Find, in terms of π, the volume of the solid generated when the shaded region is rotated through $360°$ about the x-axis. **(7 marks)**

28 **a** Show that the equation

$$\cos(x + \tfrac{\pi}{3}) - \sin(x - \tfrac{\pi}{6}) = 0,$$

can be rewritten as

$$\tan x = \frac{1}{\sqrt{3}}.$$ **(5 marks)**

b Solve the equation

$$\cos(x + \tfrac{\pi}{3}) - \sin(x - \tfrac{\pi}{6}) = 0$$

for x in the interval $^-\pi \le x \le \pi.$ **(2 marks)**

29   The function f is defined by

$$f : x \to \frac{4-3x}{3x+8}, \quad x \in \mathbb{R}, \ x \neq -\tfrac{8}{3}.$$

   a Find $f^{-1}(2)$.   **(3 marks)**

   b Solve the equation $f(x) = x$.   **(4 marks)**

30   **a**   Prove the identity

$$(\cos x + \sin x)^2 - (\cos x - \sin x)^2 \equiv 2 \sin 2x. \qquad \textbf{(4 marks)}$$

   Given that

$$a = \cos 22.5° + \sin 22.5°, \text{ and}$$
$$b = \cos 22.5° - \sin 22.5°,$$

   b use the identity in part **a** to find the value of $(a^2 - b^2)$,   **(2 marks)**

   c find the value of $(a^2 + b^2)$.   **(3 marks)**

   Given also that

$$\tan 22.5° = \sqrt{2} - 1,$$

   d show that $\dfrac{a}{b} = \sqrt{2} + 1$.   **(6 marks)**

31   The half-life of a substance is the time it takes for half of any mass of the substance to decay.

The mass, m grams, that remains after a mass of m_0 grams of Carbon-14 has decayed for t years is given by

$$m = m_0 e^{-kt},$$

where k is a positive constant.

Given that the half-life of Carbon-14 is 5720 years,

   a find the value of k correct to 4 significant figures.   **(4 marks)**

A human bone is discovered in an archaeological dig. It is found to contain approximately 40% of the mass of Carbon-14 that it would probably have contained originally.

   b Estimate the age of the bone correct to the nearest 500 years.   **(4 marks)**

32   **a**   Prove that in the series expansion of $(1 - \tfrac{x}{2})^n(1 + \tfrac{x}{2})^n$, where n is a positive integer, all odd powers of x have coefficients of zero.   **(4 marks)**

   b Given that the first three terms in the expansion of $(1 + ax + bx^2)^5$ in ascending powers of x are

$$1 - 5x + 20x^2,$$

      i find the values of a and b,

      ii find the coefficient of x^3 in the expansion.   **(8 marks)**

33 **a** Find the values of x in the interval $0 \le x \le 2\pi$ for which

$$2\tan^2 x - 3\sec x = 0,$$

giving your answers in terms of π. **(6 marks)**

b Find the values of y in the interval $0 \le y \le 360°$ for which

$$3\cos 2y - 4\sin y = 1,$$

giving your answers correct to an appropriate degree of accuracy. **(6 marks)**

34 **a** Sketch the curve $y = \ln x$. **(2 marks)**

The region enclosed by the curve $y = \ln x$, the line $x = 4$ and the x-axis is rotated through $360°$ about the x-axis to form a solid, S.

b Show that the volume, V, of S is given by

$$V = \pi \int_1^4 (\ln x)^2 \, dx.$$ **(1 mark)**

c Use the trapezium rule with 3 intervals of equal width to estimate V, giving your answer correct to 1 decimal place. **(6 marks)**

35 **a** Factorise the expression

$$xy + x + y + 1.$$ **(1 mark)**

b Hence prove that the equation

$$xy + x + y = 36,$$

has no positive integer solutions. **(5 marks)**

36

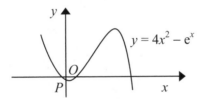

The diagram shows the curve $y = 4x^2 - e^x$ which crosses the y-axis at the point P.

a Find an equation of the tangent to the curve at P. **(4 marks)**

The tangent to the curve at P meets the curve again at the point with x-coordinate α.

b Find the integer N such that $N < \alpha < N + 1$. **(5 marks)**

c Show that the curve has a stationary point with x-coordinate β, where $3 < \beta < 4$. **(3 marks)**

d Use an iteration of the form

$$x_{n+1} = \ln(kx_n),$$

with $x_0 = 3.5$ to find β correct to 3 significant figures. **(4 marks)**

Answers

Exercise 1S   Skills Practice

1 **a** $\frac{3}{2x-1}$ **b** $\frac{x^2-2}{x+3}$ **c** $\frac{2}{t-1}$ **d** $\frac{3}{x+3}$

   e $\frac{y+1}{2y}$ **f** $\frac{2(a-1)}{a+2}$ **g** $\frac{2x-1}{2(x+1)}$ **h** $\frac{5+x}{2(1-x)}$

2 **a** $\frac{x}{2(x-3)}$ **b** $\frac{6y}{(y-3)(y-4)}$ **c** $\frac{x-1}{2x(2x+1)}$

   d $\frac{2x}{3(x-1)}$ **e** $\frac{2a(a+2)}{(a-1)^2}$ **f** $\frac{x+2}{3x-1}$

3 **a** $\frac{7t-2}{t(t-1)}$ **b** $\frac{2(x^2+x+3)}{(x+3)(x+1)}$

   c $\frac{10x-3}{2(x-2)(2x-1)}$ **d** $\frac{13x+15}{x(x^2-9)}$

   e $\frac{5y+2}{2y(y+4)(y-2)}$ **f** $\frac{11x^2-14x-7}{(2x-1)(x^2-4)}$

4 **a** -8, 2 **b** -3, 2 **c** $\frac{1}{3}$ **d** $\frac{1}{2}$, 4

5 **a** $y = \frac{2-x}{3}$ **b** $y = \frac{x(x-3)}{2(x+3)}$

   c $y = x + 1$ **d** $y = 3x + 5$

6 **a** $\frac{x+2}{x^2-9}$ **b** $\frac{2(x^2+1)}{x(3x+1)}$

Exercise 1E   Exam Practice

1 $\frac{t-3}{t-2}$

2 **a** $\frac{x(x-1)}{2x-3}$ **b** $-\frac{1}{2}$

3 **a** $y = 3x - 4$

4 **b** $\frac{(x-3)(x+4)}{2x-5}$

5 $2 \pm \sqrt{6}$

6 **b** $(1, \pm2), (-1, \pm2\sqrt{2})$

Exercise 2S   Skills Practice

1 **a** 7, 10, 13 **b** 6, 18, 54 **c** 1, 3, 7
   d 7, $\frac{15}{2}$, $\frac{31}{4}$ **e** 7, 23, 87 **f** -2, 12, -16

2 **b** $\frac{13}{4}$

3 **a** $u_n = u_{n-1} - 3$ **b** $u_n = 5u_{n-1}$
   c $u_n = 2u_{n-1} - 1$ **d** $u_n = 3u_{n-1} + 1$

4 **a** 17, 82, 407 **b** 4, 8, 24
   c 9, 7, $\frac{17}{3}$ **d** 2, 14, 50

5 **a** $-\frac{1}{2}$, $-\frac{3}{4}$, $-\frac{7}{8}$, $-\frac{15}{16}$ converging to -1
   b -2, 6, -2, 6 oscillating between 6 and -2
   c 2, 5, 14, 41 diverging
   d 4, $3\frac{1}{4}$, $3\frac{1}{16}$, $3\frac{1}{64}$ converging to 3

6 $\frac{3}{2}$

7 **a** $6 + k$, $18 + 4k$ **b** $6 - 2k$, $4k - 6$
   c $k - 2$, $k^2 - 2k - 2$ **d** $3k$, $3k^2 - 2k$

8 5

Exercise 2E   Exam Practice

1 **a** $\frac{5}{4}$ **b** 65

2 **a** $4k^2 - 6k - 6$ **b** $-\frac{3}{2}$, 3

3 **a** 16 **b** 1391

4 **a** $a = \frac{5}{2}$, $b = -2$ **b** $105\frac{1}{2}$

5 **a** -5

6 **a** $2 + \frac{1}{3}k$, $\frac{2}{3} + \frac{4}{9}k$

Exercise 3S   Skills Practice

1 $1 + 3x + 3x^2 + x^3$

2 **a** $1 + 6x + 12x^2 + 8x^3$
   b $1 - 3x + 3x^2 - x^3$
   c $1 - 6x + 12x^2 - 8x^3$
   d $1 + \frac{3}{2}x + \frac{3}{4}x^2 + \frac{1}{8}x^3$
   e $1 + 9y + 27y^2 + 27y^3$
   f $1 + 3y^2 + 3y^4 + y^6$
   g $1 - 18y + 108y^2 - 216y^3$
   h $1 + 6y^4 + 12y^8 + 8y^{12}$

3 **a** $1 + 4x + 6x^2 + 4x^3 + x^4$
   b $1 + 12x + 54x^2 + 108x^3 + 81x^4$
   c $1 - \frac{8}{3}x + \frac{8}{3}x^2 - \frac{32}{27}x^3 + \frac{16}{81}x^4$
   d $1 + 8x^{-1} + 24x^{-2} + 32x^{-3} + 16x^{-4}$
   e $1 + 5x + 10x^2 + 10x^3 + 5x^4 + x^5$
   f $1 - 10x + 40x^2 - 80x^3 + 80x^4 - 32x^5$
   g $1 + 15x^2 + 90x^4 + 270x^6 + 405x^8 + 243x^{10}$
   h $1 - 6x + 15x^2 - 20x^3 + 15x^4 - 6x^5 + x^6$

4 **a** $28 + 16\sqrt{3}$ **b** $1801 - 1527\sqrt{2}$

5 **a** $1 + 8x + 28x^2 + 56x^3$
   b $1 + 16x + 120x^2 + 560x^3$
   c $1 + 20x + 190x^2 + 1140x^3$
   d $1 + 22x + 220x^2 + 1320x^3$

6 **a** $1 + 9y + 36y^2 + 84y^3$
   b $1 - 12y + 60y^2 - 160y^3$
   c $1 - 54y + 1377y^2 - 22032y^3$
   d $1 + 5y^2 + \frac{45}{4}y^4 + 15y^6$

7 **a** $1 + 14x + 84x^2 + 280x^3$
   b 1.1487

8 **a** 126 **b** 126720 **c** 24 **d** $-^8/_3$

9 **a** $8 + 12x + 6x^2 + x^3$
b $81 - 108y + 54y^2 - 12y^3 + y^4$
c $256 + 512x + 384x^2 + 128x^3 + 16x^4$
d $1024 - 640y + 160y^2 - 20y^3 + \frac{5}{4}y^4 - \frac{1}{32}y^5$

10 **a** $6561 + 17496x + 20412x^2 + 13608x^3$
b $15625 - 18750x + 9375x^2 - 2500x^3$
c $128 + 1344x + 6048x^2 + 15120x^3$
d $59049 - 65610x + 32805x^2 - 9720x^3$

11 **a** 14 **b** 2562560 **c** 1032192 **d** 540

12 $x^4 + 8x^2 + 24 + 32x^{-2} + 16x^{-4}$

Exercise 3E   Exam Practice

1 **a** $1 + 18x + 144x^2 + 672x^3$
b 1.018145 (6 dp)

2 **a** $^2/_9 n(n-1)$ **b** 18

3 **a** $1 + 4x + 6x^2 + 4x^3 + x^4$
b $1 + 2x - 2x^2 - 8x^3 - 7x^4 - 2x^5$
c $625 - 1500x + 1350x^2 - 540x^3 + 81x^4$

4 **a** $^2/_7$

5 **a** $64 + 576x + 2160x^2 + 4320x^3$ **b** -4320

6 **a** $256 - 512x + 448x^2 - 224x^3$
b 250.925 (6 sf)

7 **a** $A = 1 + 12k^2 + 4k^4, B = 4k + 8k^3$

Exercise 4E   Exam Practice

1 **a** $A = -60, B = 1680, C = -29120$
b $-1 + 62x - 1800x^2 + 32480x^3$

2 **a** $u_2 = 9 + k, u_3 = 27 + 4k$ **b** -7

3 **a** $32 + 240x + 720x^2 + 1080x^3 + 810x^4 + 243x^5$
b -8640

4 **a** $1 - 8x + 30x^2 - 70x^3$ **b** 0.9229 (4 sf)

5 **a** 2 **b** 1747.58 (2 dp)

6 **a** $41 - 29\sqrt{2}$ **b** $-41 + 29\sqrt{2}$

7 **b** 1

8 **a** -4 **b** $-1280x^3$

9 **a** $1 + 8x + 24x^2 + 32x^3 + 16x^4$

10 **a** $^1/_2$ **b** -4

11 **a** 279 **b** 291

12 **a** $^1/_{16}x^4 + x^2 + 6 + 16x^{-2} + 16x^{-4}$ **b** 14

13 **a** $^{29}/_5$ **b** 4 **d** 2

Exercise 5S   Skills Practice

1 **a** $\log_9 81 = 2$ **b** $\log_{10} 1000 = 3$
c $\log_3 243 = 5$

2 **a** $2^4 = 16$ **b** $5^4 = 625$
c $10^6 = 1\,000\,000$

3 **a** 2 **b** 5 **c** -1 **d** 3 **e** -1
f 2 **g** -2 **h** 1 **i** 3 **j** 0
k $^1/_2$ **l** -1 **m** $^1/_4$ **n** -2 **o** $^3/_2$

4 **a** 64 **b** 125 **c** 7
d 16 **e** 1 **f** 9

5 **a** $2 \log_5 x$ **b** $12 \log_5 x$ **c** $-\log_5 x$
d $-6 \log_5 x$ **e** $^1/_2 \log_5 x$ **f** $-3 \log_5 x$

6 **a** $\log_2 15$ **b** $\log_2 3$ **c** $\log_2 81$
d $\log_2 12$ **e** $\log_2 14$ **f** $\log_2 5$

7 **a** 1 **b** 2 **c** -2 **d** 3 **e** $^1/_2$ **f** -2

8 **a** $2\log_{10} 2 + \log_{10} 3$ **b** $\log_{10} 2 + 3\log_{10} 3$
c $2\log_{10} 2 - \log_{10} 3$ **d** $-\log_{10} 2 + 3\log_{10} 3$
e $-2\log_{10} 2 + \log_{10} 3$ **f** $4\log_{10} 2 + \log_{10} 3$

Exercise 5E   Exam Practice

1 $A = 3, B = 1$

2 **a** 10.08 (2 dp) **b** 1.71 (2 dp)

3 **a** $p = 3, q = -4$ **b** 2.520 (3 dp)

4 **a** 6 **b** 1

5 **b** $^5/_2 \log_a 2$

6 1, 4

7 **a i** $3p + q$ **ii** $2q - p$ **b** $x = ^1/_3, y = 81$

Exercise 6S   Skills Practice

1 **a** 20.09 **b** 403.4 **c** 2.718
d 14.78 **e** 1.649 **f** 1.778
g 0.9031 **h** -0.1761 **i** 1.099
j -4.605 **k** 4.159 **l** 1.125

2 **a** 5 **b** 16 **c** 3 **d** 1 **e** 3 **f** -8

3 **a** e^2 **b** $e^{8/3}$ **c** $e^6 - 1$
d $^1/_4 e^5$ **e** $^1/_2(e^2 + 5)$ **f** $2e^6 - 3$

4 **a** $\ln 3$ **b** $\ln 4$
c $2 \ln 6$ **d** $^1/_3 (\ln 15 + 2)$
e $\ln ^7/_3 - 4$ **f** $^1/_2 (\ln ^3/_2 - 5)$

5 **a** 0.92 **b** 1.73 **c** 16.09
d 0.29 **e** -26.80 **f** 1.22
g -2.36 **h** -0.38 **i** 0.47

6 **a** 1.46   **b** 5.13   **c** 0.797
   d 3.95   **e** -2.18   **f** 2.15
   g 3.58   **h** 1.55   **i** -11.6
   j 5.60   **k** 2.72   **l** 8.13

7 **a** $u^2 - u - 6$ **b** 1.58

8 **a** 1.46   **b** $\frac{1}{3}$ **c** 1, 2.58
   d $\frac{3}{2}$ **e** 1.23   **f** 0.43, 0.68
   g 0, 1.58   **h** 0.32   **i** -1, 2

Exercise 6E   Exam Practice

1 **a** 2.45 (3 sf)   **b** ±3.77 (3 sf)

2 1 or 1.63 (3 sf)

3 **a** $-\frac{1}{2}e^3$

4 $x = -2$, $y = \ln 8$

5 **a** 5.95 (3 sf)   **b** 2.47 (3 sf)
   c 0.361 (3 sf)

6 2.32 (3 sf)

7 **a** 55   **b** 0.1213 (4 sf)
   c 20 (nearest min.)

Exercise 7E   Exam Practice

1 $\frac{1}{2}$

2 **a** 33.1 (3 sf)   **b** 0.759 (3 sf)

3 $A = 4$, $B = -1$

4 **b** $m = 3$, $n = 1$

5 $a = 3$, $b = -5$

6 **a** $\frac{1}{3}y^2$ **b** 0.369 (3 sf)

7 **a** $6 \ln a$

8 $x = 5$, $y = e^{-3}$

9 0.431 (3 sf)

10 **a** $p = 8$, $q = 2 \ln 2$ **b** $(\frac{3}{2} \ln 2, 2)$

11 **a** 7.23 (3 sf)   **b** 5, 20

12 e^3

13 **a** A (-1, 0), B $(\frac{1}{8}, 0)$

Exercise 8S   Skills Practice

1 **a** 5   **b** 17   **c** 8   **d** -11
   e -5   **f** 0   **g** -32   **h** $\frac{7}{4}$
   i 1   **j** $-\frac{7}{3}$ **k** 10   **l** 3

2 **a** $f(x) \in R$ **b** $f(x) \geq -2$
   c $-5 < f(x) < 3$ **d** $f(x) > 0$
   e $f(x) < 4$ **f** $\frac{1}{8} \leq f(x) \leq 2$
   g $-24 < f(x) < 24$ **h** $1 < f(x) \leq 6$

3 **a** $0 < x < 5$ **b** $-2 \leq x \leq 4$
   c $2 \leq x \leq 8$ **d** $-1 < x \leq 0$

4 **a** $(x + 3)^2 - 7$ **b** $f(x) \geq -7$

5 **a** $f(x) \geq 1$ **b** $f(x) \geq 2$
   c $f(x) \leq 11$ **d** $-10 \leq f(x) \leq 15$
   e $f(x) \geq 1$ **f** $-\frac{5}{4} \leq f(x) < 11$

6 **a** 6   **b** $-\frac{3}{2}$ **c** ±2
   d $\frac{3}{5}$ **e** $-\frac{1}{2}$, 3   **f** -3, 2

7 **a** $f^{-1}(x) \equiv \frac{1}{2}(x + 1)$, $x \in R$
   b $f^{-1}(x) \equiv 4x - 1$, $x \in R$
   c $f^{-1}(x) \equiv \frac{2}{x}$, $x \in R$, $x \neq 0$
   d $f^{-1}(x) \equiv \frac{1}{2}(x - 7)$, $x \in R$, $7 < x < 17$

9 **a** $\ln x - 1$ **b** $\frac{1}{x} - 2$ **c** $\frac{4}{3-x}$
   d $\frac{1}{2}(3^x + 1)$ **e** $\frac{3x+1}{x-1}$ **f** $\frac{5x-1}{x+2}$

10 **a** $(x - 1)^2 + 2$
   b $f^{-1}(x) \equiv 1 + \sqrt{(x - 2)}$, $x \in R$, $x > 2$

11 **a** $f^{-1}(x) \equiv -2 - \sqrt{(x + 3)}$, $x \in R$, $x \geq -3$
   b $f^{-1}(x) \equiv 6 - \sqrt{(x + 16)}$, $x \in R$, $x > -7$
   c $f^{-1}(x) \equiv -1 + \sqrt{(3 - x)}$, $x \in R$, $x < 3$
   d $f^{-1}(x) \equiv \frac{1}{2}[-3 + \sqrt{(4x + 25)}]$, $x \in R$, $x \geq -\frac{25}{4}$
   e $f^{-1}(x) \equiv 2 + \sqrt{[\frac{1}{3}(x + 12)]}$, $x \in R$, $x > -12$
   f $f^{-1}(x) \equiv \frac{1}{2}[1 + \sqrt{(4x - 3)}]$, $x \in R$, $1 \leq x \leq 7$

12 **a** 0   **b** $\frac{1}{3}(2 - e^4)$ **c** $4 - e^{-2}$ **d** $-\ln 2$

13 **a** odd   **b** neither   **c** even
   d even   **e** neither   **f** odd

14 **b** $x < -\frac{3}{2}$, $x > \frac{3}{2}$

15 **b** (-2, 0), (0, 0), (2, 0)

Exercise 8E   Exam Practice

1 **a** 5   **b** 1

2 **a** $1 + \sqrt{2}$ **b** $\frac{2x}{x+1}$, $f^{-1}(x) < 2$

3 **b** no, as f is not a 1 to 1 mapping

4 **a** $f^{-1}(x) \equiv \frac{2}{1-3x}$, $x \in R$, $x \neq \frac{1}{3}$

5 **a** $(x - 3)^2 - 2$
   c $f^{-1}(x) \equiv 3 - \sqrt{(x + 2)}$, $x \in R$, $x > 2$

6 **a** $\ln \frac{x+1}{2}$ **b** -1

Exercise 9S   Skills Practice

1 **a** 12 **b** 27 **c** 43 **d** 21 **e** 32 **f** 171

2 **a** $9 - 4x$ **b** $-4x - 6$
  c $10 - 8x^2$ **d** $2x^2 + 12x + 17$
  e $78 - 64x$ **f** $32x^2 - 96x + 74$

3 **a** 4 **b** $\pm\sqrt{5}$ **c** -1
  d $^3/_2$ **e** -4 **f** $^1/_3, ^7/_3$

4 **a** 4.95 **b** 3 **c** -125
  d 0.693 **e** 2.01 **f** -0.754

5 **a** $2x$ **b** x^2 **c** $2x^3 - 1$

6 **a** $\frac{x+3}{x}$ **b** $\frac{2x+1}{x-1}$ **c** $\frac{12x+5}{5x+2}$

7 **a** -9 **b** 1.2 **c** -1, 2

Exercise 9E   Exam Practice

1 **a** $kx + 2k^2 - 3$ **b** $^1/_2$, -3

2 **a** $f^{-1}(x) \equiv \frac{3x}{2x-1}$, $x \in \mathbb{R}$, $x \neq ^1/_2$

3 **a** $f(x) \leq 3$ **b** $3 - 2e^{-x}$ **c** $2\ln 2$

4 **a** $fg(x) \equiv 2x^2 + 15$, $x \in \mathbb{R}$, $fg(x) \geq 15$
  b -1, 3

5 **a** $f^{-1}(x) \equiv \frac{3}{2x-1}$, $x \in \mathbb{R}$, $x \neq ^1/_2$
  b -1, $^3/_2$ **c** $^5/_4$

Exercise 10S   Skills Practice

1 **a** translation by 2 in –ve x direction
  b stretch by factor of 3 in y direction
  c translation by 6 in +ve y direction
  d reflection in x-axis
  e stretch by factor of $^1/_4$ in x direction
  f reflection in y-axis

2 **a** (0, 2) **b** (0, 0) **c** (0, 0)
  d (0, 3) **e** (1, 0) **f** (0, -4)

3 **a** $(^1/_2, 0), (0, -3)$ **b** (0, 0)
  c $(^5/_2, 0), (0, -5)$ **d** $(^3/_2, 0), (0, -12)$
  e $(-^3/_4, 0), (0, -3)$ **f** $(^1/_4, 0), (0, -1)$

4 **a** (-4, 0), (0, 10) **b** (0, 0)
  c $(-^4/_3, 0), (0, 5)$ **d** (0, 0)
  e (8, 0), (0, 5) **f** $(-4, 0), (0, -^{15}/_2)$

5 **a** (-2, 5), (3, 9) **b** $(-1, 2), (^3/_2, 6)$
  c $(-2, ^4/_3), (3, 4)$ **d** (-7, 2), (-2, 6)
  e (-2, 1), (3, 9) **f** (-2, 6), (3, 2)

6 **a** e.g. translation by 1 in –ve x direction,
    then translation by 3 in +ve y direction
  b e.g. translation by 5 in +ve x direction,
    then stretch by factor of 4 in y dir'n
  c e.g. reflection in x-axis,
    then translation by 2 in +ve y direction
  d e.g. stretch by factor of $^1/_2$ in x dir'n,
    then stretch by factor of 6 in y dir'n
  e e.g. stretch by factor of $^1/_3$ in x dir'n,
    then translation by 1 in +ve x direction,
  f e.g. stretch by factor of 2 in x direction,
    then translation by 4 in –ve x direction,

9 **a** $(-^1/_3, 0), (0, 1)$ **b** $(^5/_2, 0), (0, 5)$
  c (4, 0), (0, 4) **d** (-2, 0), (2, 0), (0, 4)
  e (0, 3) **f** (-2, 0), (2, 0), (0, 2)

10 **b** $(2, 5), (-^4/_3, ^5/_3)$

11 **a** $^1/_2, 1$ **b** -2 **c** $-^3/_5, -1$
  d -6, 0 **e** $-^4/_3, 4$ **f** $-^2/_3, ^4/_3$

Exercise 10E   Exam Practice

1 **a** $(^1/_2, 0), (0, 2)$ **b** $^1/_6, ^3/_2$

2 **a** (-2, 0), (2, 0) **b** (1, 0), (5, 0)
  c (-5, 0), (-1, 0), (1, 0), (5, 0)

3 **a** 0 **b** $n \geq ^{25}/_4$

4 **a** $(^4/_3, 4), (3, 2)$ **b** (4, 4), (9, 0)
  c $(^3/_2, 4), (4, 2)$

Exercise 11E   Exam Practice

1 **a** $^1/_3$ **b** $^7/_2$

2 **a** $f^{-1}(x) \equiv \frac{3}{x-2}$, $x \in \mathbb{R}$, $x \neq 2$
  b $(0, -^3/_2)$, $x = 2$, $y = 0$

3 **a** $(^1/_2, 0), (0, 2); (0, 0)$ **b** $(^1/_3, ^2/_3), (1, 2)$

4 **a** (0, -2), (2, 4), $x = 1$
  b (3, 2), (5, 4), $x = 4$
  c (3, -1), (5, 2), $x = 4$

5 **a** $6 - x^2$ **b** $\log_3(6 - x)$ **c** 2

6 **a** (6, 0), (0, 3) **b** $2 < x < 10$

7 **a** $a = 2, b = -3$ **b** $(-^3/_2, 0), (^3/_2, 0), (0, 9)$

8 **a** (1, -2) **b** (3, 5)

9 **a** $2^{2x} - 7(2^x) + 12$ **b** 2, 1.58 (3 sf)

10 **a** (2k, 0), (0, 2k); $(-^k/_3, 0), (0, k)$
  b $-^3/_2k, ^1/_4k$

11 **a** $f(x) > 0$ **b** 0.000 335 (3 sf)   **c** $\frac{1}{2}\ln 2$

12 **a** $4 + 3\sqrt{2}$
   b $f^{-1}(x) \equiv \frac{3x}{2x+1}$, $x \in \mathbb{R}$, $x \neq -\frac{1}{2}$

13 $-\frac{1}{4}$, $\frac{11}{4}$

14 **a** $\frac{1}{4}(e^x + 1)$ **b** $f^{-1}(x) > \frac{1}{4}$
   c $h(x) \equiv 2x - \frac{1}{2}$, $x \in \mathbb{R}$

15 **a** $(x - 3)^2 - 7$
   c $f^{-1}(x) \equiv 3 + \sqrt{(x + 7)}$, $x \in \mathbb{R}$, $x \geq -7$

Exercise 12S   Skills Practice

1 **a** 2   **b** $\frac{1}{3}\sqrt{3}$ **c** $-\sqrt{2}$ **d** $-\frac{2}{3}\sqrt{3}$

2 **a** $\sqrt{2}$ **b** $-\frac{2}{3}\sqrt{3}$ **c** $\sqrt{3}$ **d** -2

3 **a** $\frac{4}{5}$ **b** $\frac{5}{4}$ **c** $\frac{5}{3}$ **d** $\frac{4}{3}$

4 **a** $(-90, -1)$, $(90, 1)$, $x = 0$
   b $(0, 2)$, $x = -90$, $x = 90$
   c $x = -90$, $x = 0$, $x = 90$
   d $(-30, 1)$, $(150, -1)$, $x = -120$, $x = 60$
   e $x = -135$, $x = 45$
   f $(-145, 3)$, $(-45, -3)$, $(45, 3)$, $(145, -3)$,
   $x = -90$, $x = 0$, $x = 90$
   g $x = -120$, $x = 60$
   h $x = 0$
   i $(0, 1)$, $x = -90$, $x = 90$

5 **a** $\frac{\pi}{6}$, $\frac{5\pi}{6}$ **b** $-\frac{\pi}{6}$, $\frac{5\pi}{6}$
   c $-\frac{3\pi}{4}$, $-\frac{7\pi}{12}$, $-\frac{\pi}{12}$, $\frac{\pi}{12}$, $\frac{7\pi}{12}$, $\frac{3\pi}{4}$
   d $\frac{2\pi}{3}$ **e** $-\frac{\pi}{6}$, $\frac{5\pi}{6}$
   f $-\frac{2\pi}{3}$, $-\frac{\pi}{3}$, $\frac{\pi}{3}$, $\frac{2\pi}{3}$

6 **a** $45°$, $225°$ **b** $137.4°$, $342.6°$
   c $68.1°$, $151.9°$, $248.1°$, $331.9°$
   d $30°$, $150°$ **e** $56.3°$, $236.3°$
   f $19.5°$, $160.5°$

7 **a** $-1 \leq x \leq 1$, $-\frac{\pi}{2} \leq y \leq \frac{\pi}{2}$
   b $-1 \leq x \leq 1$, $0 \leq y \leq \pi$
   c $x \in \mathbb{R}$, $-\frac{\pi}{2} \leq y \leq \frac{\pi}{2}$

8 **a** $\frac{\pi}{6}$ **b** $\frac{\pi}{6}$ **c** $-\frac{\pi}{4}$
   d $\frac{\pi}{4}$ **e** $\frac{\pi}{3}$ **f** $-\frac{\pi}{3}$

9 **a** $\frac{\sqrt{3}}{2}$ **b** 0.817 **c** -0.682

Exercise 12E   Exam Practice

1 $\frac{\pi}{6}$, $\frac{5\pi}{6}$, $\frac{7\pi}{6}$, $\frac{11\pi}{6}$

2 **a** $\frac{2\pi}{3}$ **b** $0 \leq f(x) \leq \pi$ **c** $-\frac{1}{2}\sqrt{2}$

3 **a** A $(90, -1)$, B $(270, -5)$
   b $41.8°$, $138.2°$ (1 dp)

4 $-75.5°$ (1 dp), 0, $75.5°$ (1 dp)

5 **a** $(\frac{2\pi}{3}, -\frac{1}{2})$, $(\frac{5\pi}{3}, \frac{1}{2})$ **b** $\frac{\pi}{3}$, π

Exercise 13S   Skills Practice

2 **a** $30°$, $150°$, $210°$, $330°$
   b $63.4°$, $243.4°$
   c $90°$, $210°$, $330°$
   d $75.5°$, $120°$, $240°$, $284.5°$
   e $63.4°$, $161.6°$, $243.4°$, $341.6°$
   f $30°$, $150°$
   g 0, $30°$, $150°$, $180°$, $210°$, $330°$, $360°$
   h $60°$, $120°$, $240°$, $300°$

6 **a** $\frac{1}{4}(\sqrt{6} + \sqrt{2})$ **b** $\sqrt{6} - \sqrt{2}$
   c $2 + \sqrt{3}$ **d** $\sqrt{6} - \sqrt{2}$

7 **a** $\sin 3A$ **b** $\cos 2A$
   c $-2 \cos (A + 2B)$ **d** $-\tan (4A + B)$

8 **a** 1, $60°$ **b** 1, $120°$
   c 2, $280°$ **d** 3, $22.5°$

9 **a** -1, $\frac{4\pi}{3}$ **b** -2, $\frac{3\pi}{4}$
   c -1, $\frac{7\pi}{8}$ **d** -1, $\frac{2\pi}{3}$

10 **a** $-\frac{12}{13}$ **b** $-\frac{33}{65}$ **c** $\frac{63}{16}$ **d** $-\frac{65}{56}$

11 **a** $\frac{\pi}{6}$, $\frac{7\pi}{6}$ **b** 2.07, 5.21
   c $\frac{\pi}{6}$, $\frac{5\pi}{6}$, $\frac{7\pi}{6}$, $\frac{11\pi}{6}$ **d** 2.95, 6.09

15 **a** $-90°$, $30°$, $90°$, $150°$
   b $-150°$, $-30°$
   c $-73.7°$, $73.7°$
   d $-180°$, $-110.7°$, $-90°$, $-69.3°$, 0, $69.3°$,
   $90°$, $110.7°$, $180°$
   e $-144.7°$, $-35.3°$, $35.3°$, $144.7°$
   f $-150°$, $-30°$, $30°$, $150°$

Exercise 13E   Exam Practice

1 **b** $9.2°$ (1 dp), $22.5°$, $99.2°$ (1 dp), $112.5°$

2 **b** π

3 **a** $(\frac{\pi}{2}, 0)$ **b** B $(\frac{\pi}{3}, \sqrt{3})$, C $(\frac{2\pi}{3}, -\sqrt{3})$

4 **a** $\frac{\pi}{2}$, $\frac{5\pi}{4}$, $\frac{3\pi}{2}$, $\frac{7\pi}{4}$
   b $19.5°$ (1 dp), $30°$, $150°$, $160.5°$ (1 dp)

5 2.43, 5.57 (2 dp)

7 **b** $\sqrt{2} - 1$

8 **a** $-\frac{1}{2}(1 + \sqrt{2})$ **b** $52.5°$, $232.5°$

9 **b** $45°$, $90°$, $135°$, $225°$, $270°$, $315°$

Exercise 14S   Skills Practice

1 **a** 5, 53.1° **b** 5, 36.9° **c** 25, 16.3°
  d $\sqrt{2}$, 45° **e** $\sqrt{13}$, 56.3° **f** $\sqrt{17}$, 14.0°

2 **a** $\sqrt{2} \cos (x - {}^{\pi}/_4)$ **b** $2 \cos (x + {}^{\pi}/_6)$
  c $-4\sqrt{2} \cos (x + {}^{\pi}/_4)$ **d** $2\sqrt{2} \cos (x - {}^{\pi}/_3)$

3 **a** e.g. $13 \sin (x + 1.18)$
  b e.g. $3\sqrt{2} \sin (x - {}^{\pi}/_4)$
  c e.g. $\sqrt{37} \cos (x + 0.17)$
  d e.g. ${}^{5}/_6 \cos (x - 0.93)$

4 **a** -10, 216.9° **b** $-\sqrt{10}$, 108.4°
  c $-3\sqrt{2}$, 199.5° **d** $-\sqrt{29}$, 67.3°

5 **a** 0, 90° **b** 12.4°, 105.7°
  c -97.3°, 129.8°
  d -153.4°, -90°, 26.6°, 90°

6 **a** 5.36 **b** π, 2π
  c 0.13, 2.22 **d** 0.55, 2.26

7 **a** (61.9, 17), (241.9, -17)
  b (67.5, $-\sqrt{2}$), (157.5, $\sqrt{2}$), (247.5, $-\sqrt{2}$),
    (337.5, $\sqrt{2}$)
  c (126.9, 0.2), (306.9, -0.2)
  d (54.5, 1.4), (234.5, -1.4)

8 **a** $\sin 4A + \sin 2A$
  b $\cos 7B + \cos 3B$
  c $2 \cos A - 2 \cos 5A$
  d $\frac{1}{2} \sin 5A - \frac{1}{2} \sin 3A$
  e $\cos (A + 2B) + \cos (A - 2B)$
  f $\frac{1}{2} \sin 4A + \frac{1}{2} \sin (2A + 2B)$

9 **a** $2 \cos 2A \cos A$
  b $2 \cos 4B \sin 2B$
  c $6 \sin 3A \sin 2A$
  d $2 \sin (A + 2B) \cos (A - 2B)$
  e $2 \cos (2A - B) \sin A$
  f $2 \cos \frac{3A+B}{2} \cos \frac{A+5B}{2}$

10 **a** 0, 60°, 120°, 180°
  b 0, 36°, 108°, 180°
  c 120° **d** 15°, 60°, 105°
  e 20°, 45°, 100°, 135°, 140°
  f 24.3°, 65.7°, 90° **g** 0, 90°, 180°
  h 0, 45°, 90°, 135°, 180°

12 **a** 0, 70.5°, 289.5°, 360° **b** 7.5°, 187.5°
  c 15°, 45°, 75°, 135°, 195°, 225°, 255°,
    315°
  d 0, 135°, 180°, 315°, 360° **e** 150°, 330°
  f 0, 30°, 90°, 150°, 180°, 210°, 270°,
    330°, 360°
  g 45°, 135°, 225°, 315° **h** 210°, 330°

13 **a** 0.30, 2.28 **b** ${}^{\pi}/_6$, ${}^{5\pi}/_6$
  c ${}^{\pi}/_{24}$ **d** 1.21, 5.07
  e 1.26, 4.40 **f** ${}^{\pi}/_5$, ${}^{3\pi}/_5$, π, ${}^{7\pi}/_5$, ${}^{9\pi}/_5$
  g 0, 4.84, 2π **h** ${}^{\pi}/_6$, ${}^{2\pi}/_3$, ${}^{7\pi}/_6$, ${}^{5\pi}/_3$

Exercise 14E   Exam Practice

1 **a** -90°, 90° **b** 0, ${}^{\pi}/_7$, ${}^{3\pi}/_7$, ${}^{2\pi}/_3$, ${}^{5\pi}/_7$, π

2 **a** $5 \sin (x - 36.9)$ **b** (0, -3)
  c B (36.9, 0), C (216.9, 0)

3 **b** ${}^{\pi}/_{24}$, ${}^{5\pi}/_{24}$, ${}^{\pi}/_2$, ${}^{13\pi}/_{24}$, ${}^{17\pi}/_{24}$

4 **a** $R = 13$, $\alpha = 22.6°$ (1 dp)
  b (11.3, 13), (101.3, -13)

5 **a** $4\sqrt{3}$ **b** ${}^{-\pi}/_2$, ${}^{-\pi}/_6$

7 **a** 0, 240° **b** 1, 120°

8 **a** ${}^{\pi}/_4$, ${}^{\pi}/_2$, ${}^{3\pi}/_4$, ${}^{5\pi}/_4$, ${}^{3\pi}/_2$, ${}^{7\pi}/_4$
  b 40°, 80°, 90°, 160°

9 **a** $R = {}^{1}/_2$, $\alpha = 36.9°$ (1 dp)
  b 8.1°, 278.1° (1 dp)

Exercise 15E   Exam Practice

1 **b** ${}^{\pi}/_8$, ${}^{3\pi}/_8$, ${}^{5\pi}/_8$, ${}^{7\pi}/_8$

2 **a** $R = 2$, $\alpha = {}^{\pi}/_3$ **b** ${}^{\pi}/_4$, ${}^{5\pi}/_4$

3 **a** (0, ${}^{2}/_3\sqrt{3}$) **b** (${}^{\pi}/_{12}$, 1)
  c (${}^{7\pi}/_{12}$, -1) **d** $x = {}^{\pi}/_3$

4 **b** 12

5 **a** 60°, 300° **b** 30°, 150°

6 **b** ${}^{-\pi}/_2 \le f(x) \le {}^{\pi}/_2$ **c** ${}^{\sqrt{3}}/_2$ **d** 2

7 **a** $\sqrt{2} \cos (2x - {}^{\pi}/_4)$
  b 0, ${}^{\pi}/_4$, π, ${}^{5\pi}/_4$, 2π

8 **b** 70.5° (1 dp), 180°, 289.5° (1 dp)

9 **a** -135°, -104.0° (1 dp), 45°, 76.0° (1 dp)

11 **a** $a = 3$, $b = 2$ **b** (π, 1) **c** 0.421 (3 sf)

12 **a** 5°, 65°, 125° **b** ${}^{4\pi}/_3$, ${}^{5\pi}/_3$

13 **b** 0, ${}^{4\pi}/_5$, ${}^{4\pi}/_3$, ${}^{8\pi}/_5$

Exercise 16S   Skills Practice

1 **a** e^x **b** $2e^x$ **c** $\frac{1}{3}e^x$
   d $\frac{1}{x}$ **e** $\frac{1}{x}$ **f** $\frac{5}{x}$

2 **a** $2x + 2e^x$ **b** $\frac{1}{x}$
   c $4 + \frac{1}{2}e^x$ **d** $\frac{3}{x} - 5x^{3/2}$
   e $5e^x + \frac{4}{x}$ **f** $3x^2 + 3 - 6e^x$

3 **a** $1 - \frac{2}{3}e^t$ **b** $t^{-1} + 2t^{-3}$
   c $6e^t + 2t^{-1}$ **d** $\frac{1}{2}t^{-1/2} + 2 + 5e^t$
   e $\frac{1}{2}t^2 + 5t^{-1}$ **f** $t^{-1} + 2e^t + \frac{3}{4}t^{-1/4}$

4 **a** $e^x - 6x$ **b** $-2x^{-5/3} - 3x^{-2}$
   c $-6x^{-2} - 3e^x$

5 **a** $\frac{2}{3}$ **b** $-\ln 2$ **c** $\frac{1}{2}, 3$

6 **a** $(\ln 3, 3\ln 3 + 2)$ max
   b $(\frac{1}{2}, 3)$ min
   c $(2, 2\ln 2 + 1)$ max
   d $(9, 6\ln 3 - 6)$ max
   e $(-\ln 2, 4 + 4\ln 2)$ min
   f $(1, -7 - 6\ln 3)$ max, $(3, -15)$ min

7 **a** $y = 6x - 8$ **b** $y = 3ex - 1$
   c $y = 3 - 7x$ **d** $y = (1 - e^4)x + 3e^4$

8 **a** $y = \frac{1}{2}x + 5$
   b $y = 2 + \ln 3 - x$
   c $y = -2e^{-3}x + 6e^{-3} + \frac{1}{2}e^3$
   d $y = 6x - 16\ln 2 - 44$

Exercise 16E   Exam Practice

1 **a** $3x - y + 1 = 0$ **b** $(\frac{1}{5}, 1 - \ln \frac{2}{5})$

2 **a** $-4x^{-2}$ **b** 2

3 **a** $(\ln 2, 5 - 4\ln 2)$ **b** 9

4 **a** $10 + 5\ln 2 - e^3$ **b** $(2.23, 4.15)$ (3 sf)

5 **b** $y = x + 4$

6 **a** $6x - 19 + \frac{3}{x}$ **b** $\frac{1}{6}, 3$
   c $(\frac{1}{6}, -\frac{37}{12}), (3, 3\ln 18 - 30)$

7 **b** $y = -\frac{1}{3}x + 4 + \frac{2}{3}\ln 3$ **c** $\frac{20}{3}\ln 3$

8 **a** $1 + \sqrt{2}$

Exercise 17S   Skills Practice

1 **a** $e^x + c$ **b** $5e^x + c$ **c** $\frac{3}{4}e^x + c$
   d $\ln|x| + c$ **e** $3\ln|x| + c$ **f** $\frac{1}{4}\ln|x| + c$

2 **a** $2y^2 + e^y + c$ **b** $\frac{1}{3}y^3 - \ln|y| + c$
   c $3e^y + 2\ln|y| + c$
   d $\frac{2}{3}\ln|y| - y + \frac{3}{2}y^2 + c$
   e $\frac{1}{5}e^y + \frac{2}{3}y^{3/2} + c$
   f $y - 2y^{1/2} + \frac{1}{4}\ln|y| + c$

3 **a** $x^2 - 3e^x + c$
   b $3r - \ln|r| + \frac{1}{r} + c$
   c $2\ln|x| - 5x - \frac{3}{2}x^2 + c$
   d $y - 2\ln|y| + c$
   e $\frac{5}{2}e^t + \frac{1}{6}t^3 + c$
   f $\frac{1}{3}x - \frac{4}{3}\ln|x| - \frac{2}{3}x^{-1} + c$

4 **a** $3x^2 - 2\ln x$ **b** $e^x - 5x + 1$
   c $6x + \ln 3x$ **d** $2x^2 + \ln 5x - 2$
   e $x^2 - 5x + e^x$ **f** $2\ln x - 3\sqrt{x} + 7$

5 **a** $e^2 - 3$ **b** $6 + 2\ln 2$
   c $2\ln 3 + 10$ **d** $6 - 2\ln 2$
   e $\frac{14}{3} - e + e^{-1}$ **f** $14 + \ln 2$
   g $\frac{13}{6} - 2\ln 3$ **h** $7 - 3e^2$
   i $\frac{77}{8} - 4\ln 2$

6 $e^2 - 5$

8 **a** $x = e^y$

9 **a** $8 + 3\ln 3$ **b** $3e - \frac{10}{3}$
   c $\frac{1}{2}e(e^3 - 1) + 6\ln 2$ **d** $\frac{14}{3} + 2\ln 2$
   e $\frac{1}{2}(e^4 - 1)$ **f** $2\ln 5$

11 $9\pi(e - e^{-1})$

12 **a** 81π **b** $\frac{16}{15}\pi$
   c $\frac{4}{3}\pi$ **d** $\frac{81}{10}\pi$
   e $\pi(6 - 8\ln 2)$ **f** $\pi(e^2 + 8e - 1)$

13 **a** $x = \frac{1}{16}y^4$

14 **a** $\pi(e^4 - 1)$ **b** $\frac{381}{7}\pi$
   c $\frac{16}{15}\pi$ **d** $\pi(\frac{122}{9} + \frac{3}{2}\ln 3)$

Exercise 17E   Exam Practice

1 **a** $3x^2 - 6x - x^{-1} + 2x^{-2}$
   b $\frac{152}{27} - 2\ln 3$

2 **b** $\frac{13}{12}\pi$

3 **a** $\frac{1}{2}x^2 - 2x + 3e^x + c$
   b $\frac{1}{2}x^2 - 2x + 3e^x - 7$

4 **a** $x^2 - 6x^{-1} + 12 - 8x$

5 **a** $\frac{4}{3}\sqrt{x} + \frac{1}{3}\ln|x| + c$

6 **a** 9 **b** $(\frac{1}{2}, 0), (4, 0)$

8 **b** $x = \frac{1}{3}e^y$

Exercise 18E   Exam Practice

1   **a** $x - 4\ln|x| - 4x^{-1} + c$ **b** $^{48}/_5 - 4\ln 5$

2   **a** $^1/_4$

3   **b** $-^1/_4$

4   $3\ln 3 - 4$

5   **a** $(4, 0), (0, -2), (0, 2)$ **c** 8π

6   $^3/_2$

7   **a** $y = 2 - 8x$
    b $(\ln 5, 10 - 10\ln 5)$

8   **a** $y = ^1/_2 x + ^1/_2$ **b** $^1/_4(8\ln 2 - 1)$

11 **a** 9.61 (3 sf)

Exercise 19S   Skills Practice

1   **a** -1.52, 1.39   **c** -1, 1

3   **a** 1   **b** 4   **c** 1
    d 2   **e** 7   **f** 4

5   **a** 8   **b** 22   **c** -8
    d 13   **e** -25   **f** 127

6   **b** -1, 3

7   0.4844, 0.4862, 0.4860, 0.4860;
    root = 0.486

8   **a** converges on different root
    b converges on root in interval (2, 3)
    c diverges

9   **a** 2.11

10 **a** 0.41   **b** 1.07   **c** 0.82   **d** 6.85

12 **a** 2.42   **b** -1.23

13 **a** 1.50   **b** 2.76   **c** 0.451   **d** -0.316

Exercise 19E   Exam Practice

1   **b** 0.317 (3 dp)   **c** 6

2   **b i** -0.3333, -0.2835, -0.2924, -0.2908,
           -0.2911
    c 2.67 (3 sf)

3   **a** 4   **c** 1.92 (3 sf)

Exercise 20S   Skills Practice

1   21.4

2   **a** 80   **b** $^{256}/_3$, 6.25%

4   **a** $^1/_6(3 + 2\sqrt{2} + 2\sqrt{3})$ **b** $^{67}/_{30}$
    c $^{43}/_2 - 2\ln 2 - \ln 3$ **d** $^1/_8\pi^2(\sqrt{2} + 1)$

5   **a** 8.97   **b** 3.75   **c** 19.4
    d 5.56   **e** 0.789   **f** 10.1

Exercise 20E   Exam Practice

1   13.87 (2 dp)

2   **a** $x = 2 + e^{3y}$

3   2.50 (3 sf)

4   **a** $^\pi/_6, ^{5\pi}/_6$

Exercise 21E   Exam Practice

1   **a** $y = ^1/_3 x + 3$ **c** 17

2   **a** $^{3\pi}/_2$ **b** 3π

3   **b** 37.2

4   **b** 1.195 (4 sf)

5   **b** 0.666 (3 dp)   **c** less

6   **b** 1.172 (4 sf)   **c** -2.33 (3 sf)

7   53.5

Exercise 22S   Skills Practice

4   **a** false   **b** true   **c** false   **d** false
    e true   **f** true   **g** false

Exercise 22E   Exam Practice

4   **a** false   **b** true   **c** false

9   **a** false   **b** false   **c** true

Exercise 23E   Exam Practice

1 **a** 0.565 (3 sf)   **b** -9.71 (3 sf)

2 **b** $\frac{3}{8} + \frac{1}{2}\cos 2x + \frac{1}{8}\cos 4x$

3 **b** 1.14 (3 sf)

4 2

5 $\frac{-2y}{3(y+3)}$

6 **a** $9 - 12x^{-1/2} + 4x^{-1}$

7 **a** $p = \frac{3}{2}, q = 2$

    b $f^{-1}(x) \equiv \frac{3x+1}{2x-1}$, $x \in R$, $x \neq \frac{1}{2}$

    d $x \in R$, $x \neq 3$

8 **b** $x = 0.01$, $0.000\,54$ (2 sf)

9 **a** 86°C   **b** 38°C
    c 30 mins   **d** 22°C

10 **a i** all terms are 2 **ii** diverges
    c $u_n = 3^{n-1}u_1$

11 2

12 **a** ln 2   **b** 0.6970 (4 dp)

13 **a** $10.8 \sin(180t + 33.7)°$ **b** 0.078

14 **b** $(\frac{1}{2}, -\frac{5}{2})$, (2, 5)

15 **a** (0, 0), (3, 0), (2, 3)
    b (-6, 0), (0, 0), (6, 0), (-4, 3), (4, 3)
    c (-6, 0), (0, 0), (-2, $\frac{3}{2}$)

16 **a** $x(x + 1)(x - 1)$

17 **a** $x^3 - 6x^2 + 12x - 8$
    b $\frac{2x^3 - 6x^2 + 8}{x^2}$ **d** (-1, 27)

18 **b** $\frac{\pi}{12}, \frac{5\pi}{12}, \frac{3\pi}{4}, \frac{13\pi}{12}, \frac{17\pi}{12}, \frac{7\pi}{4}$

19 **a** 0.792 (3 sf)   **b** $\sqrt{3}$

20 **b** k **c** $\frac{1}{2}$

22 **b** $\frac{3}{2}$ **c** $\frac{81}{16}$

23 **a** $-\frac{2}{3} \leq x \leq \frac{3}{2}$
    b $(-\frac{2}{3}, 0)$, $(\frac{3}{2}, 0)$, (0, 6)

24 **c** $\alpha = 60°$, $R = 2$

25 **a** $\frac{1}{2}$, 4
    b i $\frac{1}{4}$, 16   **ii** $\frac{\pi}{12}, \frac{5\pi}{12}, \frac{13\pi}{12}, \frac{17\pi}{12}$

26 $\frac{1}{3}a$, $5a$

27 **a** (1, -1), (4, 2)   **b** $\frac{16}{3}\pi$

28 **b** $-\frac{5\pi}{6}, \frac{\pi}{6}$

29 **a** $-\frac{4}{3}$ **b** -4, $\frac{1}{3}$

30 **b** $\sqrt{2}$ **c** 2

31 **a** 0.000 121 2 (4 sf)
    b 7500 yrs (nearest 500 yrs)

32 **b i** $a = -1, b = 2$ **ii** -50

33 **a** $\frac{\pi}{3}, \frac{5\pi}{3}$
    b 19.5° (1 dp), 160.5° (1 dp), 270°

34 **c** 8.3 (1 dp)

35 **a** $(x + 1)(y + 1)$

36 **a** $y = -x - 1$ **b** 4   **d** 3.26 (3 sf)